THE MASTER BUILDER

The Plays of Ibsen

1828–1906

with their dates of composition

CATILINE, 1849
THE WARRIOR'S BARROW, 1849–50
NORMA, 1851
ST JOHN'S EVE, 1852
LADY INGER OF OESTRAAT, 1854
THE FEAST AT SOLHAUG, 1855
OLAF LILJEKRANS, 1856
THE VIKINGS AT HELGELAND, 1857
LOVE'S COMEDY, 1862
THE PRETENDERS, 1863
BRAND, 1865
PEER GYNT, 1867
THE LEAGUE OF YOUTH, 1868–69
EMPEROR AND GALILEAN, 1864–73
THE PILLARS OF SOCIETY, 1875–77
A DOLL'S HOUSE, 1879
GHOSTS, 1881
AN ENEMY OF THE PEOPLE, 1882
THE WILD DUCK, 1884
ROSMERSHOLM, 1886
THE LADY FROM THE SEA, 1888
HEDDA GABLER, 1890
THE MASTER BUILDER, 1892
LITTLE EYOLF, 1894
JOHN GABRIEL BORKMAN, 1896
WHEN WE DEAD AWAKEN, 1899

HENRIK IBSEN

The Master Builder

NEWLY TRANSLATED FROM THE NORWEGIAN BY

Michael Meyer

RUPERT HART-DAVIS
Soho Square London
1961

PRINTED IN GREAT BRITAIN
BY WESTERN PRINTING SERVICES LTD BRISTOL

CONTENTS

Introduction   7

The Master Builder   31

English Stage History   109

Note on the Translation   126

INTRODUCTION

Ibsen wrote *The Master Builder* in Christiania in 1892, at the age of sixty-four. It was the first play he had written in Norway since *The Pretenders* twenty-nine years before.

The previous summer (1891) he had left his home in Munich for a holiday to the North Cape. While he was there, he decided to stay in Christiania over the winter; and as things turned out he stayed there for the remaining fifteen years of his life.

There were several reasons for this decision to settle again in his native country after twenty-seven years abroad. He told Georg Brandes that it would be more convenient for him financially, but Fru Ibsen later said she thought it was because he wanted to die in Norway. During his visit in 1885 he had been unwell, and had then spoken of settling there; and in the beginning of 1890 he had a severe attack of influenza, which may have helped to remind him that he was no longer young. Moreover, he still had the obsessive longing for the sea which twice recently had driven him northwards (in 1885 and 1887). A further reason was that his son Sigurd was now very active in Norwegian politics and was being spoken of as a likely Foreign Minister as soon as Norway should obtain her independence from Sweden. Ibsen was very devoted to his son, and although he did not, in his old age, take much interest in politics he now found himself acclaimed by both the right and the left wing parties. Life in Norway had seemed insufferable to him when he had been impoverished and unsuccessful. Now that he was a national hero, it held certain attractions. So he stayed.

Departing from his usual routine of writing only during the

summer and autumn, he began work on a new play the following March (1892). Before the spring was over, however, he scrapped everything he had written, and did not start again until August. We do not know how long he took to complete his new draft, but the unusual number of small mistakes and omissions suggest that he wrote it very rapidly. By 30 October he had finished his revisions and sent his fair copy off to the printer; it contains fewer divergencies from the original draft than in any other of his plays.

The Master Builder was published by Gyldendals of Copenhagen on 12 December 1892. People everywhere were puzzled by it, as they had been puzzled by his two preceding plays, *The Lady from the Sea* and *Hedda Gabler*, but for a different reason. Some new element had entered into Ibsen's work. It had been perceptible in *Hedda Gabler*, but in *The Master Builder* it was more than perceptible; it stuck out for all to see. Even without Freud to suggest the implications of all that talk about towers and spires that made an old man feel giddy and a young girl hear harps in the air, *The Master Builder* seemed primarily to be a play about sexual passion. People speculated as to what new influence could have entered into the aged playwright's life to turn his thoughts so sharply in this direction, and not until after Ibsen's death in 1906 was the answer given.

In that year Georg Brandes published a series of letters which Ibsen had written between October 1889 and December 1890 (i.e., twenty-nine to fifteen months before he began *The Master Builder*) to a young Viennese girl named Emilie Bardach. These revealed that in the summer of 1889, when Ibsen was sixty-one and Emilie eighteen, they had met at Gossensass in the Austrian Tyrol and that some kind of infatuation had resulted; whether this had been mutual or one-sided was not quite clear. They had corresponded for over a year and then Ibsen, gently but firmly, had told her not to write to him any more.

Shortly after these letters appeared a friend of Ibsen, the German literary historian Julius Elias, published an account of a conversation he had had with Ibsen concerning Emilie

8

Bardach which seemed to put the incident into proportion. This conversation had taken place in Berlin in February 1891, over lunch, while Ibsen was waiting for a train:

"An expansive mood came over Ibsen and, chuckling over his champagne glass, he said: 'Do you know, my next play is already hovering before me—in general outline, of course. One thing I can see clearly, though—an experience I once had myself—a female character. Very interesting—very interesting.' Then he related how he had met in the Tyrol a Viennese girl of very remarkable character, who had at once made him her confidant. The gist of it was that she was not interested in the idea of marrying some decently brought-up young man; most likely she would never marry. What tempted, fascinated and delighted her was to lure other woman's husbands away from them. She was a demonic little wrecker; she often seemed to him like a little bird of prey, who would gladly have included him among her victims. He had studied her very, very closely. But she had had no great success with him. 'She did not get hold of me, but I got hold of her—for my play. Then I fancy she consoled herself with someone else.'"

That seemed to settle the matter. Ibsen's version of Emilie's character, or Elias's report of it, was generally accepted, and Emilie Bardach went down to history while she was still a young woman (she survived the Second World War) as a predatory little monster more or less identical with Hilde Wangel.

In 1923, however, two remarkable articles entitled "Ibsen and Emilie Bardach" were published in the American *Century Magazine*. The author was an Ibsen enthusiast named Basil King. In 1908, while travelling in Europe, he had met Emilie, then a woman of thirty-seven, "gentle of manner, soft of voice, dressed with the distinction of which Viennese women have long possessed the art . . . going to Paris for the spring, to London for the season, and often to Scotland for country-house gatherings." She allowed King to see, and in due course to quote from, the diary she had kept during the time she had known and corresponded with Ibsen. These articles caused no particular sensation at the time, interest in Ibsen being rather low in England and America during the early twenties; there seems, however, no reason to doubt the authenticity of the diary extracts, and they go much further than Ibsen's (or Elias's) account of the incident to explain the stormy and dynamic quality of his last five plays, after the apparent optimism of *The Lady from the Sea*.

Ibsen had come to Gossensass in July 1889. He had holidayed there on several previous occasions, but this was his first visit for five years, and the town had decided to celebrate his return by naming his old look-out on the hill the Ibsenplatz. There was a festal procession, and Ibsen, despite the steep ascent, climbed at the head of it and "received with friendliness and dignity all the homage that was accorded him." Emilie Bardach wrote in her diary (5 August 1889):

"The weather is very bad and we cannot make any excursions. The day of the Ibsen fête has been the only fine one; but I washed my hair and could not go. After the concert, however, I made his acquaintance in a way quite delightful."

On the outskirts of the town there was a valley named the Pflerschtal, with a stream flowing through it and a view of mountains and glaciers. While walking here, Ibsen saw a girl seated on a bench with a book. He came and sat beside her, and learned her name, her parentage, her home residence, and the fact that in Gossensass they lived so near together that his windows looked into hers. A few days later, she ran into him at a dull birthday party. "It is a pity," she noted, "that German gives him so much difficulty, as apart from that we understand each other so well."

She fell ill and, a few days later, Ibsen came to see her, climbing over the garden gate to do so. "He remained with me a long while, and was both kind and sympathetic." A little later: "We talk a great deal together. His ardour ought to make me feel proud." Then:

"Ibsen has begun to talk to me quite seriously about myself. He stayed a long time with me on Saturday, and also again this evening. Our being so much together cannot but have some painful influence over me. He puts such strong feeling into what he says to me. His words often give me a sensation of terror and cold. He talks about the most serious things in life, and believes in me so much. He expects from me much, much, much more than I am afraid he will ever find. Never in his whole life, he says, has he felt so much joy in knowing anyone. He never admired anyone as he admires me. But all in him is truly good and noble! What a pity it is that I cannot remember all his words! He begs me so intensely to talk freely to him, to be absolutely frank with him, so that we may become fellow-workers together."

Next she writes: "Mama has just gone out, so that I have the room to myself. At last I am free to put down the incredible things of these recent days. How poor and insufficient are words! Tears say these things better. Passion has come when it cannot lead to anything, when both of us are bound by so many ties. Eternal obstacles! Are they in my will? Or are they in the circumstances? . . . How could I compare anything else that has happened to an outpouring like this? It could never go so far, and yet—" She swings off on to Baron A., the only lover who afforded a standard of comparison. "But how much calmer *he* was, how inarticulate, beside this volcano, so terribly beautiful! Yesterday afternoon, we were alone together at last! Oh, the words! If only they could have stamped themselves on my heart more deeply and distinctly! All that has been offered me before was only the pretence at love. This is the true love, the ideal, he says, to which without knowing it he gave himself in his art. At last he is a true poet through pain and renunciation. And yet he is glad of having known me—the most beautiful! the wonderful! Too late! How small I seem to myself that I cannot spring to him!"

Neither Ibsen's wife nor Emilie's mother suspected what was afoot. But:

"The obstacles! How they grow more numerous, the more I think of them! The difference of age!—his wife!—his son! —all that there is to keep us apart! Did this have to happen?

Could I have foreseen it? Could I have prevented it? When he talks to me as he does, I often feel that I must go far away from here—far away!—and yet I suffer at the thought of leaving him. I suffer most from his impatience, his restlessness. I begin to feel it now, even when we are in the salon, quite apart from each other. . . .

"It all came to me so suddenly! I noticed for the first time how he began to change his regular ways of life, but I didn't know what it meant. Of course I was flattered at his sympathy, and at being distinguished among the many who surround him, eager for a word. . . ."

An early snowstorm came, and the guests at Gossensass began to leave. Emilie realized they would soon have to part. "And I have nothing to give him, not even my picture, when he is giving me so much. But we both feel it is best outwardly to remain as strangers. . . . His wife shows me much attention. Yesterday I had a long talk with his son . . .

"I am reading Ibsen's *Love's Comedy*, but if anyone comes I am seen holding Beaconsfield's *Endymion* in my hands. Nearly everyone has gone. The days we have still to spend can now be counted. I don't think about the future. The present is too much. We had a long talk together in the morning, and after lunch he came again and sat with me. What am I to think? He says it is to be my life's aim to work with him. We are to write to each other often; but what am I to write?"

Ibsen confided his feelings to two ladies. One fainted; another described the scene to Emilie as "beautiful and terrible as a thunderstorm. She wonders that I do not lose my head. She says that she herself would have been absolutely overcome. This consoles me. I do not seem so weak."

Did something happen between Ibsen and Emilie on 19 September, and if so was it anything like what Hilde Wangel describes as having happened between her and Solness on another 19 September? Nearly forty years later, in 1927, Emilie told A. E. Zucker that Ibsen had never kissed her; perhaps with Ibsen, as with Solness, these things only happened in his mind. Next day, 20 September, he wrote in

Emilie's album: *"Hohes, schmerzliches Glück—um das Unerreichbare zu ringen!"*—"High and painful fate—to struggle for the unattainable!"

A week later, on 27 September, Emilie noted in her diary: "Our last day at Gossensass. Then nothing but memory will remain. Two weeks ago, memory seemed to Ibsen so beautiful, and now— He says that tomorrow he will stand on the ruins of his happiness. These last two months are more important in his life than anything that has gone before. Am I unnatural in being so terribly quiet and normal? . . . Last evening, when Mama went to talk to his wife, he came over and sat at our table. We were quite alone. He talked about his plans. I alone am in them—I, and I again. I feel quieter because he is quieter, though yesterday he was terrible."

That night, at 3 a.m., the express from Verona to Vienna passed through Gossensass, and Ibsen left on it. The same night, Emilie wrote in her diary:

"He means to possess me. This is his absolute will. He intends to overcome all obstacles. I do what I can to keep him from feeling this, and yet I listen as he describes what is to lie before us—going from one country to another—I with him—enjoying his triumphs together. . . . Our parting was easier than I had feared."

Emilie told Zucker in 1927 that Ibsen had, in Gossensass, "spoken to her of the possibility of a divorce and of a subsequent union with her, in the course of which they were to travel widely and see the world." The last entry in her diary would seem to bear this out. Once back in Munich, however, Ibsen seemed to resign himself to the impossibility of going through with such a plan. Perhaps he feared the scandal; perhaps he felt a duty towards his sickly and ageing wife, who had stood so firmly by him during the long years of failure; perhaps he reflected that the difference of forty-three years between their ages was too great; perhaps, away from Gossensass, he felt old. Probably all these considerations influenced him. At any rate, his letters from Munich to Emilie in Vienna are no more than those of an affectionate old man to a charming schoolgirl (though we must bear in mind that he is writing in a foreign language which "gives him much difficulty", that he was always an extremely inhibited letter-writer, and that he must have been very careful not to commit himself on paper).

München, Maximilianstrasse 32.
7 October 1889.

With my whole heart I thank you, my beloved Fräulein, for the dear and delightful letter which I received on the last day of my stay at Gossensass, and have read over and over again.

There the last autumn week was a very sad one, or it was so to me. No more sunshine. Everything—gone. The few remaining guests could give me no compensation for the brief and beautiful end-of-summer life. I went to walk in the Pflerschthal. There there is a bench where two can commune together. But the bench was empty and I went by without sitting down. So, too, the big salon was waste and desolate. . . . Do you remember the big, deep bay-window on the right from the verandah? What a charming niche! The flowers and plants are still there, smelling so sweetly—but how empty!—how lonely!—how forsaken!

We are back here at home—and you in Vienna. You write that you feel surer of yourself, more independent, happier. How glad I am of these words! I shall say no more.

A new poem begins to dawn in me. I want to work on it this winter, transmuting into it the glowing inspiration of the summer. But the end may be disappointment. I feel it. It is my way. I told you once that I only corresponded by telegraph. So take this letter as it is. You will know what it means. A thousand greetings from your devoted.—H.I.

The "poem" may have been *Hedda Gabler*, which he was to write the following year, or it may have been *The Master Builder* itself. He did not in fact write *The Master Builder* until three years later, but he may have conceived it at this stage and then deliberately have put it aside until he could consider it with more detachment.

14

Emilie's diary, 8 October 1889:

"A few words before I go to bed. I have good news. Today, at last, came Ibsen's long-expected letter. He wants me to read between the lines. But do not the lines themselves say enough? This evening I paid Grandmama a quite unpleasant visit. The weather is hot and stuffy and so is Papa's mood. In other days, this would have depressed me; but now I have something to keep me up."

We do not know how she replied to Ibsen, for he did not preserve her letter. On 15 October, however, he writes again:

I receive your letter with a thousand thanks—and have read it, and read it again. Here I sit as usual at my desk, and would gladly work, but cannot do so.

My imagination is ragingly at work, but is always straying to where in working hours it should not. I cannot keep down the memories of the summer, neither do I want to. The things we have lived through I live again and again—and still again. To make of them a poem is for the time being impossible.

For the time being?

Shall I ever succeed in the future? And do I really wish that I could and would so succeed?

For the moment, at any rate, I cannot—or so I believe. That I feel—that I know.

And yet it must come. Decidedly it must come. But will it? or can it?

Ah, dear Fräulein—but forgive me!—you wrote so charmingly in your last—no, no! God forbid!—in your *previous* letter you wrote so charmingly: "I am not Fräulein for you"—So, dear Child,—for that you surely are for me—tell me—do you remember that once we talked about Stupidity and Madness—or, more correctly, *I* talked about it —and you took up the role of teacher, and remarked, in your soft, musical voice, and with your far-away look, that there is always a difference between Stupidity and Madness . . . Well, then, I keep thinking over and over again: Was it a Stupidity or was it Madness that we should have come together? Or was it both Stupidity *and* Madness? Or was it neither?

I believe the last is the only supposition that would stand the test. It was a simple necessity of nature. It was equally our fate. . . . Your always devoted—H.I.

On receipt of this letter, Emilie wrote in her diary: "I left it unopened till I had finished everything, and could read it quietly. But I was not quiet after reading it. Why does he not tell me of something to read which would feed my mind instead of writing in a way to inflame my already excited imagination? I shall answer very soberly."

Ibsen to Emilie, 29 October 1889:

I have been meaning every day to write you a few words, but I wanted to enclose the photograph. This is still not ready, and my letter must go off without it. . . .

How charmingly you write! Please keep sending me a few lines, whenever you have a half hour not good for anything else.

So you leave my letters unopened till you are alone and quite undisturbed! Dear Child! I shall not try to thank you. That would be superfluous. You know what I mean.

Don't be uneasy because just now I cannot work. In the back of my mind, I am working all the time. I am dreaming over something which, when it has ripened, will become a poem.

Someone is coming. Can write no further. Next time a longer letter. Your truly devoted H.I.

Emilie's diary: "I wrote to him on Monday, very late at night. Though I was tired, I did not want to put off doing so, because I had to thank him for the books I received on Sunday. The same evening I had read *Rosmersholm*, parts of which are very fine. I have to make so many duty calls, but this and a great many other things I can stand better than I used to. They are only the outward things; my inner world is something very different. Oh, the terror and beauty of having him care about me as he never cared about anyone else! But when he is suffering he calls it *hohes, schmerzliches Glück*—high and painful fate!"

Ibsen to Emilie, 19 November 1889:

At last I can send you the new picture. I hope you may find it a better likeness than the one you have already. A German sketch of my life will appear within a few days, and you will receive it at once. Read it when you have the time. It will tell you my story up to the end of last year.

Heartfelt thanks for your dear letter; but what do you think of me for not having answered it earlier? And yet— you know it well—you are always in my thoughts, and will remain there. An active exchange of letters is on my side an impossibility. I have already said so. Take me as I am.

I am greatly preoccupied with the preparations for my new play. Sit tight at my desk the whole day. Go out only towards evening. I dream and remember and write. To dream is fine; but the reality at times can still be finer. Your most devoted H.I.

On the back of the photograph stood the inscription: "*An die Maisonne eines Septemberlebens*"—"To the May sun of a September life."

Ibsen to Emilie, 6 December 1889:

Two dear, dear letters have I had from you, and answered neither till now. What do you think of me? But I cannot find the quiet necessary to writing you anything orderly or straight-forward. This evening I must go to the theatre to see *An Enemy of the People*. The mere thought of it is a torture. Then, too, I must give up for the time being the hope of getting your photograph. But better so than to have an unfavourable picture. Besides, how vividly your dear, serene features remain with me in my memory! The same enigmatic princess stands behind them. But the enigma itself? One can dream of it, and write about it—and that I do. It is some little compensation for the unattainable—for the unfathomable reality. In my imagination I always see you wearing the pearls you love so much. In this taste for pearls I see something deeper, something hidden. I often think of it. Sometimes I think I have found the interpretation—and then again not. Next time

I shall try to answer some of your questions; but I myself have so many questions to ask you. I am always doing it—inwardly—inaudibly. Your devoted H.I.

In her diary, Emilie repeats his words: "It is some little compensation for the unattainable, for the unfathomable reality."

Ibsen to Emilie, 22 December 1889:

How shall I thank you for your dear and delightful letter? I simply am not able to, at least not as I should like. The writing of letters is always hard for me. I think I have told you so already, and you will in any case have noticed it for yourself.

I read your letter over and over, for through it the voice of the summer awakens so clearly. I see—I experience again—the things we lived together. As a lovely creature of the summer, dear Princess, I have known you, as a being of the season of butterflies and wild flowers. How I should like to see you as you are in winter! I am always with you in spirit. I see you in the Ring Strasse, light, quick, poised like a bird, gracious in velvet and furs. In soirées, in society, I also see you, and especially at the theatre, leaning back, a tired look in your mysterious eyes. I should like, too, to see you at home, but here I don't succeed, as I haven't the data. You have told me so little of your home-life—hardly anything definite. As a matter of fact, dear Princess, in many important details we are strangers to each other. . . .

More than anything I should like to see you on Christmas night at home, where I suppose you will be. As to what happens to you there, I have no clear idea. I only imagine—to myself.

And then I have a strange feeling that you and Christmas don't go well together. But who knows? Perhaps you do. In any case accept my heartfelt wishes and a thousand greetings. Your always devoted H.I.

On the same day, 22 December 1889, Emilie wrote to Ibsen, enclosing at last her photograph; it is one of the only two letters from her which survived.

Sunday.

Here is the photograph—very unlike the original—to wish you a happy Christmas. Are you satisfied with it? Do you think it is a good one? I don't think any better picture of me can be expected, but I hope it may give you some small pleasure. Now I must confess that I have had this proof for a fortnight—I kept it back so long in order to send it to you as a Christmas greeting. It was hard to keep it a secret from you for so long, but I wanted to have some little thing to contribute to the lovely holiday. Should I play no role at all in that? It's bad enough that I am not able to do more. In spite of my "*Nicht Rönnaug*," a few weeks ago I painted a trifle for you which would have been altogether pointless if it did not recall Gossensass. I used to buy little deer bells there, and since I so often met you on my way home from my study trip to the Strassberg ruins I perpetuated the picture on one of these bells. Then I waited for your son to come here as I would have liked to give it to him to take to you—but he didn't come and it seemed too small a thing to make a business of sending it. I will be silent for a while, then I will be able to tell you better about that. How much longer are you going to make me wait? This detailed letter which is to tell me so much—but no—don't think this is a reproach—I don't mean it like that. I will send a Christmas greeting to your wife—I must write a few words just to her.

Well, once more many tender wishes and regards.
    Sincerely,
      Emilie.

Ibsen to Emilie, 30 December 1889:

Your lovely and charming picture, so eloquently like you, has given me a wholly indescribable joy. I thank you for it a thousand times, and straight from the heart. How you have brought back, now in midwinter, those brief sunny summer days!

So, too, I thank you from the heart for your dear, dear letter. From me you must expect no more than a few words.

I lack the time, and the necessary quiet and solitude, to write to you as I should like. . . .

Ibsen to Emilie, 16 January 1890:

How sorry I am to learn that you, too, have been ill. But what do you think! I had a strong presentiment that it was so. In my imagination I saw you lying in bed, pale, feverish, but sweet and lovely as ever. . . . How thankful I am that I have your charming picture!

Ibsen to Emilie, 16 February 1890:

Long, very long, have I left your last, dear letter—read and read again—without an answer. Take today my heartfelt thanks for it, though given in very few words. Henceforth, till we see each other face to face, you will hear little from me, and very seldom. Believe me, it is better so. It is the only right thing. It is a matter of conscience with me to end our correspondence, or at least to limit it. You yourself should have as little to do with me as possible. With your young life you have other aims to follow, other tasks to fulfil. And I— I have told you so already—can never be content with a mere exchange of letters. For me it is only half the thing; it is a false situation. Not to give myself wholly and unreservedly makes me unhappy. It is my nature. I cannot change it. You are so delicately subtle, so instinctively penetrating, that you will easily see what I mean. When we are together again, I shall be able to explain it more fully. Till then, and always, you will be in my thoughts. You will be so even more when we no longer have to stop at this wearisome halfway house of correspondence. A thousand greetings. Your H.I.

She replied to him the following day:

Please forgive me for writing again so soon. All these days I had been intending to write to you, for it is part of my nature to feel anxious about persons to whom I am deeply attached, if I do not hear from them for a longish time. Possibly this is a petty characteristic, but it is impossible to control one's feelings. Nevertheless, I mean to control mine, and since I knew how sensitive you are in this respect I came halfway to meet you. Yes, I knew very well that you are an unwilling letter-writer, and from time to time I even felt that you might find my letters a nuisance. All the same, your last letter has shaken me badly, and I have needed all my self-control to conceal my feelings. But I don't want this to prevent you from carrying out your intentions. I certainly do not wish you to write to me frequently and, since you wish it, I shall also refrain. However, I cannot allow myself to prescribe the problems and the moods to which, as you say, I should surrender myself in my young life. What I have so often told you remains unaltered and I can never forget it. Unfortunately the fact remains that I cannot surrender myself completely, nor taste unalloyed enjoyment. Forgive me for drawing you into a conflict with fate. That is ungrateful of me, seeing that you have so often said to me that whatever happens we shall remain good friends, and that I must hold fast to that. And is it friendship not to know if the other is ill or well, happy or wretched? And then can I prevent the thought coming to me that *you* want to avoid seeing me again, and anyhow, if you do not write, how am I to know where we can find each other again? Well, I'll be very, very patient; I can wait, but I shall suffer very much if I don't get a line or a book from you from time to time, or some other proof that you think of me. I am not noble enough to dispense with such little proofs of your interest.

Ought I to be ashamed of my frankness? Will you think less of me for not wishing to give up what has made me so much happier and more contented through all these months? I know you a little and that is why I understand so much that is in you, but I am sure that *your conscience* should never hinder you from continuing to write to me. By so doing you only show your kindness. I will try to understand all other reasons that may prevent you from writing and certainly I don't want you to act against your feelings. What a multitude of things there are to write about, but you do not wish me to write, even though I should not expect an answer.

Tonight I have an invitation to a ball—with friends; I never go out in public. When I am there I shall allow myself to think a little about you because I often find parties like these extremely uninspiring, unless I have something of my own to fall back on. Anyhow, I mean to go, if I can.

With love,

Emilie.

Emilie made no entries in her diary for four days after receiving the news that Ibsen wished to break off their correspondence. Then she writes of balls, singing lessons, domestic duties. Then suddenly: "What is my inner life after Ibsen's letter? I wrote at once and henceforth will be silent, silent." Ten days later: "Will he never write any more? I cannot think about it. Who could? And yet, not to do so is in his nature. In his very kindness there is often cruelty."

For seven months he did not write to her. During this time, he was struggling with *Hedda Gabler*.[1] On 29 June he wrote to the Swedish poet Carl Snoilsky that he had been hoping to spend the summer in the Tyrol but had encountered difficulties in the writing of his new play and did

---

[1] It may be noted that in the first draft of *Hedda Gabler*, in the scene when Hedda shows Lœvborg her honeymoon photographs, the dialogue runs as follows:

HEDDA. What was this little village called?

TESMAN. What? Let me think. Oh, that's Gossensass, on the Brenner Pass. We stayed a day there—

But when he revised the play Ibsen struck out all mention of Gossensass, so that the dialogue reads:

HEDDA. Do you remember this little village?

TESMAN. Oh, that one down by the Brenner Pass? We stayed a night there—

Basil King comments: "Though in that play there is no outward trace of Emilie Bardach, both must be present as vital forces. . . . It is safe to say that to the girl in Vienna *Hedda Gabler* owes much of its marvellous élan. She was not in it, but she was behind it, as, according to his English biographer [Edmund Gosse] she was to be behind everything else for the rest of the poet's life."

not want to leave Munich until he had overcome them. He had in fact been planning to return to Gossensass and from the references in his letters to "when we are together again" I think it is fair to assume that he hoped to meet Emilie there (we must remember that her parents knew nothing of her feelings for Ibsen).

In September, he broke his silence to write Emilie a letter of sympathy on the bereavement of her father, with some news of himself and his family, but no more. On 30 December, he writes briefly to thank her for a Christmas present:

I have duly received your dear letter, as well as the bell with the beautiful picture. I thank you for them, straight from the heart. My wife finds the picture very pretty. But I beg you, for the time being, not to write to me again. When conditions have changed, I will let you know. I shall soon send you my new play. Accept it in friendship—but in silence. How I should love to see you and talk with you again! A Happy New Year to you and to Madame your mother. Your always devoted H.I.

She did not write to him again, nor did the meeting to which they had both looked forward so eagerly ever take place. For seven years, there was no contact between them. Then, on his seventieth birthday, an occasion of great celebration in Scandinavia, she sent him a telegram of congratulation. His letter of reply was the last message that passed between them:

Christiania, 15 March 1898.
Herzlich liebes Fräulein!

Accept my most deeply felt thanks for your message. The summer in Gossensass was the happiest, the most beautiful, in my whole life.

I scarcely dare to think of it—and yet I must think of it always. Always!

Your truly devoted H.I.

It is against this background that we must read *The Master Builder*. Other influences, of course, intrude into it. He had returned to Norway by the time he began to write it, and took pains to make Hilde almost ostentatiously Norwegian in her speech and manners. He had by this time struck up a friendship with a young Norwegian pianist, Hildur Andersen, the daughter of old friends from his Bergen days; she seems to have possessed many of the qualities which he admired in Emilie, notably the combination of eagerness and sensitivity, and it may be that her name, Hildur, caused him to remember the Hilde whom he had created as a minor character in *The Lady from the Sea* and whom he now resurrected, ten years older, to play a more important role. Aline Solness is plainly based on Ibsen's own wife, and the relationship between the Solnesses bears an uncomfortable resemblance to that which appears to have existed at this time in the Ibsen household. Shortly after their return to Norway, Ibsen's mother-in-law, Magdalene Thoresen (the original of Ellida in *The Lady from the Sea*), wrote: "They live splendidly, and have an elegant home, though all is pretty much in Philistine style. They are two lonely people—each for himself—each absolutely for himself."

Ibsen destroyed his preliminary notes for *The Master Builder* and whatever work he may have done on the play in the spring of 1892, apart from a curious rhymed poem of twelve lines. As William Archer pointed out "It is said to have been his habit, before setting to work on a play, to crystallize in a poem the mood which then possessed him", and this is the only one of these poems which has survived. It is dated 16 March 1892 I quote it in A. G. Chater's translation:

> They dwelt, those two, in so cosy a house
> In autumn and winter weather.
> Then came the fire—and the house was gone.
> They must search the ashes together.

For down in the ashes a jewel lies hid
Whose brightness the flames could not smother,
And search they but faithfully, he and she,
'Twill be found by one or the other.

But e'en though they find it, the gem they lost,
The enduring jewel they cherished—
She ne'er will recover her vanished faith
Nor he the joy that has perished.[1]

A few months before Ibsen began work on *The Master Builder*, the young novelist Knut Hamsun had delivered three lectures in Christiania on the decadence of modern literature, in the course of which he had particularly attacked the "big four" of Norwegian letters, Ibsen, Bjørnson, Alexander Kielland and Jonas Lie. An invitation was sent to Ibsen and, to the consternation of those present, he attended all three lectures, sitting in seat number one in the front row. He is reported to have sat "quiet and serious, with unmoved countenance. . . . His strong blue eyes did not leave the speaker for a minute." It may well have been the memory of Hamsun's invective that suggested Solness's fear of "youth banging on the door." In passing, one may note that in his lectures Hamsun had insisted on the necessity of probing into the dark and unconscious corners of the human mind, and that Ibsen, in *The Master Builder* and the three plays which followed, was to do this; though he had already made a beginning in *The Lady from the Sea*.

The character of Solness was the nearest thing to a self-portrait that Ibsen had yet attempted, though he was to follow it with two equally merciless likenesses in *John Gabriel Borkman* and *When We Dead Awaken*. He admitted in a speech a few years later that "Solness is a man who is somewhat related to me." Ibsen had long regarded himself

[1] Ibsen in fact incorporated this poem in his first draft of *Little Eyolf*, which he wrote two years after *The Master Builder*; Allmers reads it to Rita in the third act. It contained one amendment: the penultimate line ends with the word peace (*ro*) instead of faith (*tro*). But he deleted the poem in revision.

as a builder and his plays as works of architecture. As early as 1858, in a poem entitled *Building Plans*,[1] he had compared the artist to a master builder; and when Erik Werenskiold, seeing him looking at some new buildings in Christiania, asked him: "You are interested in architecture?" Ibsen replied: "Yes; it is, as you know, my own trade." Ibsen, like Solness, had always had a fear of looking down from a great height, or into a deep chasm, and this had become worse as he had grown older. Solness's ruthlessness, his readiness to sacrifice the happiness of those nearest to him for the sake of his ambition, his longing for and fear of youth, and the conflict in him between aesthetic and ethical demands— all these were Ibsen's too. Moreover, during Ibsen's last years in Munich he continually raised the subject of hypnotism, of how one human being could gain power over the mind of another, and how unexpressed wishes sometimes translated themselves into actions. This curiosity, too, had already manifested itself in *The Lady from the Sea*.

Two drafts of the play survive, written one after the other in the autumn of 1892. The second of these corresponds more or less exactly with the final printed version, and the first, unlike most of Ibsen's early drafts, contains no very significant variations. One sentence, however, deleted in revision, reveals how closely Ibsen identified himself with Solness. In the second act, when Solness is telling Hilde how success came to him, Ibsen originally made him conclude with the

[1] BUILDING PLANS (1858)

I remember as well as if it were yesterday
The evening when, in the paper, I saw my first poem in print.
I sat there in my garret puffing my pipe
And dreaming dreams of blest complacency.

"I shall build a cloud-castle. It shall shine over the North.
Two wings shall it have; one little and one great.
The great wing shall shelter an immortal poet;
The small wing shall be a young girl's bower."

I thought this a noble and harmonious plan.
But then confusion entered into it.
As the master grew sane, the castle went all crazy.
The great wing shrank; the small fell into ruins.
(translation Michael Meyer).

words: "And now, at last, they have begun to talk of me abroad." Viewed with this in mind, the theory propounded soon after the publication of the play that, to quote Archer, "the churches which Solness sets out by building doubtless represents Ibsen's early romantic plays, the 'homes for human beings' his social dramas, while the houses with high towers, merging into 'castles in the air', stand for those spiritual dramas, with a wide outlook over the metaphysical environment of humanity, on which he was henceforth to be engaged" seems less fanciful than might at first appear.

Even since childhood, Ibsen had been fascinated by towers. In the memoirs of his childhood and youth which he had compiled a few years previously to help Henrik Jaeger in the writing of his authorized biography, Ibsen had mentioned that the house in which he was born "stood exactly opposite the front of the church, with its high flight of steps and its conspicuous tower" from which the watchman used to proclaim the hour at night. A poodle also, lived in the tower; "it had fiery red eyes, but was rarely visible. Indeed, so far as I know, he was never seen but once". One New Year's morning, just as the watchman shouted "One" through the opening in the front of the tower, the poodle appeared behind him and looked at him with his fiery eyes, whereupon the watchman fell down into the market place and was killed. "From that night, the watchman never calls 'One' from the church tower at Skien." It was from the opening in this tower, Ibsen continues, that he received "the first conscious and permanent impression on my mind. My nurse one day took me up the tower and allowed me to sit on the ledge outside. . . . I perfectly recollect how amazed I was at looking down on the tops of the hats of the people below." His mother happened to look up from her window, saw him there, shrieked and fainted "as people used to do in those days. . . . As a boy, I never went across the market-place without looking up at the tower window. I always felt as though the opening and the church poodle were some special concern of mine."

In a letter written to his sister Hedvig on 13 March 1891,

when he was already planning *The Master Builder*, Ibsen recalled that "the house where I was born and lived the first years of my childhood, and the church, the old church with its christening-angel under the roof, are now burned down. All that my earliest memories are associated with—it was all burned." These feelings are strongly echoed in Solness's account of the burning of his wife's ancestral home; and the christening-angel (which was lowered when a child was to be christened) may possibly be the original of Aline's dolls.

Shortly before he left Munich that summer, Ibsen heard the legend of the master builder who had built St Michael's Church there and had thrown himself down from the tower of the church because he was afraid the roof would not hold. Ibsen said he thought the legend must have arisen in Scandinavia, and when the others observed that every famous cathedral in Germany had the same legend he replied that this must be because people felt instinctively that a man could not build so high without paying the penalty for his hubris.

The publication of *The Master Builder* was eagerly awaited throughout Europe. English, French and German translations appeared almost simultaneously with the original, the German translation being by Ibsen's son, Sigurd. Translations into Russian, Dutch, Polish and Bohemian followed shortly afterwards. Great arguments developed as to the meaning of the play. As a contemporary put it: "While one person sees Solness as Ibsen himself, another sees him as Bjørnson, a third as a symbol of the right wing party, a fourth as a symbol of the left and its leader; a fifth sees Solness as a symbol of Man rising in rebellion against God; a sixth sees the play as a conflict between youth and the older generation." Some sought to identify Solness with Bismarck, while *The Saturday Review* in London decided that he was meant as a portrait of Mr Gladstone, and that the play was full of references to the Irish question. Ibsen, when asked which of these interpretations was true, replied that the play merely portrayed people whom he had known and that he could not understand what everyone was arguing about.

The Master Builder received its first performance at the Lessing Theatre in Berlin on 19 January 1893, after the usual public reading in London (in Norwegian) to secure performing copyright. Before the end of the month it had also been staged in Bergen, Copenhagen, Gothenburg, Trondheim, Stockholm, Åbo and Helsingfors. London[1] and Chicago saw it in February, and Rome in April. It has remained one of Ibsen's most admired and most frequently performed plays.

In 1908 Emilie Bardach saw *The Master Builder* for the first time, in Munich. After the performance, she said: "I didn't see myself; but I saw him. There is something of me in Hilde; but in Solness, there is little that is not Ibsen."

MICHAEL MEYER.

See page 109.

ACKNOWLEDGMENTS

Permission to quote from Emilie Bardach's letters has been kindly granted by Gyldendal Norsk Forlag of Oslo.

Mrs Reginald Orcutt has given her permission for the use of the quotations from Basil King's articles, "Ibsen and Emilie Bardach".

CHARACTERS

HALVARD SOLNESS,   master builder.

ALINE SOLNESS,   his wife.

DOCTOR HERDAL,   a family physician.

KNUT BROVIK,   sometime architect, now assistant to Solness.

RAGNAR BROVIK,   his son, a draughtsman.

KAJA FOSLI,   book-keeper, niece to Knut Brovik.

HILDE WANGEL

LADIES

PEOPLE IN THE STREET

The action takes place in SOLNESS's house.

ACT ONE

A plainly furnished office in SOLNESS'S *house. In the left-hand wall, double doors lead out to the hall. To the right is a door leading to the inner rooms of the house. In the rear wall, an open door leading to the drawing office. Downstage left, a high desk with books, papers and writing materials. Upstage of the door, a stove. In the right-hand corner, a sofa, with a table and two or three chairs. On the table, a water carafe and glasses. Downstage right, a smaller table, with a rocking chair and an armchair. Lighted lamps are on the table in the drawing office, and also on the table in the corner and on the desk.*

Inside the drawing office sit KNUT BROVIK *and his son,* RAGNAR, *busy with plans and calculations.* KAJA FOSLI *stands at the desk in the office, writing in the ledger.* KNUT BROVIK *is a thin old man with white hair and beard, dressed in a somewhat worn but carefully preserved black tail coat. He wears spectacles and a white cravat, which has turned rather yellow.* RAGNAR BROVIK *is in his thirties, well dressed, fair haired, with a slight stoop.* KAJA FOSLI *is a slender girl in her early twenties, neatly dressed but of sickly appearance. She wears a green shade over her eyes. For a while, all three work in silence.*

BROVIK (*gets up suddenly from the drawing table, as though in distress, and breathes heavily and with difficulty as he comes forward into the doorway*): No, I can't go on with this much longer.

KAJA (*goes over to him*): It's really bad tonight, isn't it, uncle?

BROVIK: Yes, it seems to grow worse every day.

RAGNAR (*has got up, and comes closer*): You'd better go home, father. Try to get a little sleep—

31

BROVIK (*impatiently*): Go to bed? Do you want me to suffocate?

KAJA: Take a little walk, anyway.

RAGNAR: Yes, do that. I'll come with you.

BROVIK: I'm not going before he comes! This evening I'm going to have it out with—(*Bitterly*)—with *him*. The master builder!

KAJA (*anxiously*): Oh, no, uncle, let that wait.

RAGNAR: Yes, better wait, father.

BROVIK (*laughs with difficulty*): I can't afford to wait very long.

KAJA (*listens*): Ssh! I can hear him coming up the steps.

All three go back to their work again. Short pause. HALVARD SOLNESS, *master builder, enters through the hall door. He is an oldish man, strong and vigorous, with close-cut, curly hair, dark moustache, and dark, thick eyebrows. He is dressed in a grey-green jacket, buttoned up, with high collar and broad lapels. He has a soft grey hat on his head, and two or three portfolios under his arm.*

SOLNESS (*in the doorway, points towards the drawing office and asks in a whisper*): Have they gone?

KAJA (*softly, shakes her head*): No.

She takes off her eyeshade. SOLNESS *walks across the room, throws his hat on a chair, puts the portfolios on the table by the sofa and comes back towards the desk.* KAJA *continues writing, but seems nervous and ill at ease.*

SOLNESS (*aloud*): What's that you're entering there, Miss Fosli?

KAJA (*starts*): Oh, just something that—

SOLNESS: Let me see. (*Leans over her, pretending to look at the ledger, and whispers*) Kaja?

KAJA (*softly as she writes*): Yes?

SOLNESS: Why do you always take off that eyeshade when I come in?

KAJA: It makes me look so ugly.

SOLNESS (*smiles*): And you don't want to look ugly, Kaja?

KAJA (*half glances up at him*): Not for anything! Not to you!

32

SOLNESS (*strokes her hair gently*): Poor, poor little Kaja!
KAJA (*moves her head away*): Ssh! They can hear you!

SOLNESS *strolls across the room to the right, turns, and stands by
the door to the drawing office*

SOLNESS: Has anyone been asking for me?
RAGNAR (*stands up*): Yes, that young couple who want the
villa built out at Løvstrand.
SOLNESS (*growls*): Oh them? Well, they'll have to wait. The
plan's not come clear in my mind yet.
RAGNAR (*comes closer, a little diffidently*): They were very
anxious to get the drawings as soon as possible.
SOLNESS: Yes, that's what they all say.
BROVIK (*looks up*): They're longing to get into a place of their
own.
SOLNESS: Oh, yes, yes. I know that sort. They'll take anything
with four walls and a roof over it. Anywhere to lay their
heads. That's not what I call a home. If that's what they
want, let them go to someone else. Tell them that next
time they come.
BROVIK (*pushes his spectacles up on to his forehead and stares
amazed*): Someone else? Would you let the contract go?
SOLNESS (*impatiently*): Yes, damn it, yes! If it comes to the
point. I'd rather that than build rubbish. Anyway, I don't
know these people.
BROVIK: Oh, they're sound enough. Ragnar knows them.
He's a friend of the family. Very sound people.
SOLNESS: Oh, sound, sound! That's not what I mean. Great
God, don't you understand me either? (*Angrily*) I don't
want to have anything to do with people I don't know. As
far as I'm concerned, they can go to anyone they like.
BROVIK (*gets up*): Are you serious?
SOLNESS: Yes. For once.

He walks across the room. BROVIK *glances at* RAGNAR, *who
makes a warning gesture, then goes into the other room.*

BROVIK: May I have a few words with you?
SOLNESS: Certainly.

BROVIK: Go inside for a moment, Kaja.

KAJA (*uneasy*): But, uncle—

BROVIK: Do as I say, child. And close the door after you.

KAJA *goes unwillingly into the drawing office, glances anxiously and pleadingly at* SOLNESS, *and closes the door.*

BROVIK (*lowers his voice*): I don't want the children to know how seriously ill I am.

SOLNESS: Yes, you look rather poorly these days.

BROVIK: I haven't much longer. My strength gets less every day.

SOLNESS: Sit down for a moment.

BROVIK: Thank you, may I?

SOLNESS (*moves the armchair a little*): Here. Well?

BROVIK (*sits down with difficulty*): It's this question of Ragnar. That's what weighs most on my mind. What's to become of him?

SOLNESS: Your son? He'll stay here with me, for as long as he wants to.

BROVIK: But that's just it. He doesn't want to. He doesn't feel he can—now.

SOLNESS: Well, he's doing quite well for himself, I should have thought. Still, if he wants a little more, I wouldn't be unwilling to—

BROVIK: No, no, that's not it. (*Impatiently*) It's time he was given the chance to do something on his own.

SOLNESS (*not looking at him*): Do you think he's got the ability?

BROVIK: That's what's so dreadful. I've begun to have doubts about the boy. In all these years you've never uttered so much as a single word of encouragement about him. But it must be there. I can't believe he hasn't got the ability.

SOLNESS: But he doesn't know anything. Not really. Except how to draw.

BROVIK (*with suppressed hatred*): You didn't know much either, when you were working for me. But you managed to get started all right. (*Breathes heavily*) Fought your way up. Put me out of business—and plenty of others.

SOLNESS: Yes—things worked out for me.

34

BROVIK: That's right. Everything worked out nicely for you. But surely you won't let me die without seeing what Ragnar can do? And I would like to see them married before I go.

SOLNESS (*sharply*): Does she want that?

BROVIK: Not Kaja so much. It's Ragnar—he talks about it every day. (*Pleadingly*) You must—you *must* help him to stand on his own feet now! I must see the lad do something on his own! Do you hear?

SOLNESS (*angrily*): But damn it, I can't conjure contracts out of the air for him.

BROVIK: He could get a commission right away. A nice big job.

SOLNESS (*startled, uneasy*): Could he?

BROVIK: If you agree.

SOLNESS: What kind of a job would that be?

BROVIK (*a little diffidently*): He could build that villa out at Lœvstrand.

SOLNESS: That! But I'm going to build that myself.

BROVIK: Oh, you don't really want to do that.

SOLNESS: Don't want to? Who dared to say that?

BROVIK: You said so yourself, just now.

SOLNESS: Oh, never mind what I *say*. Could Ragnar get the contract?

BROVIK: Yes. He knows the family, you see. And then, he's —just for the fun of it, you know—he's made drawings and estimates and so on—

SOLNESS: And these drawings—are they satisfied with them? These people who are going to live there?

BROVIK: Yes. If only you'd just look through them and approve them, they—

SOLNESS: They'd like Ragnar to build their home for them?

BROVIK: They were very taken with his idea. They thought it was so new and original.

SOLNESS: Oh! New. Not the old-fashioned junk I build?

BROVIK: They thought this was—different.

SOLNESS: So it was Ragnar they came to see—while I was out.

BROVIK: They came to talk to you. And to ask if you'd be willing to give way—

SOLNESS: I? Give way for your son!

BROVIK: Rescind the contract, they meant.

SOLNESS: What's the difference? (*Laughs bitterly*) So that's it! Halvard Solness is to retire! Retire to make way for younger men! For apprentices! Make way for the young! Make way! Make way!

BROVIK: Good heavens, there's room in this town for more than one—

SOLNESS: Oh, there's not so much room round here either. But that's not the point. I shall never give way. I shall never make way for anyone! Not of my own freewill, Never, never!

BROVIK (*gets up with difficulty*): Won't you let me die in peace? Happy—believing in my son? Won't you let me see him do one thing on his own?

SOLNESS (*turns half aside and mutters*): Don't ask me that now.

BROVIK: Yes, answer me! Must I die so poor?

SOLNESS (*seems to fight with himself, then says, quietly but firmly*): You must die as best you can.

BROVIK: So be it. (*Walks away*).

SOLNESS (*follows him, almost desperately*): I can't do otherwise, don't you understand? I am what I am. And I can't create myself anew.

BROVIK: No, no. You can't do that. (*Stumbles and stops by the sofa table*) May I have a glass of water?

SOLNESS: Of course. (*Pours one out and hands it to him*).

BROVIK: Thank you. (*Drinks and puts the glass down.* SOLNESS *goes over to the door of the drawing office and opens it*).

SOLNESS: Ragnar, you'd better take your father home.

RAGNAR *gets up quickly. He and* KAJA *come into the office.*

RAGNAR: What is it, father?

BROVIK: Take my arm. Let's go.

RAGNAR: All right. Put your coat on, Kaja.

SOLNESS: Miss Fosli must stay. For a few minutes. I have a letter to write.

BROVIK (*looks at* SOLNESS): Good night. Sleep well—if you can.

SOLNESS: Good night.

BROVIK *and* RAGNAR *go out through the front door.* KAJA *goes across to her desk.* SOLNESS *stands with bowed head near the armchair on the right.*

KAJA (*uncertainly*): Have you got a letter—?

SOLNESS (*curtly*): No, no, of course not. (*Looks sharply at her*) Kaja!

KAJA (*quietly, frightened*): Yes?

SOLNESS (*points commandingly with a finger towards the floor*): Come here. At once!

KAJA (*unwillingly*): Yes.

SOLNESS (*still in the same tone*): Closer!

KAJA (*obeying him*): What do you want me to do?

SOLNESS (*looks at her for a moment*): Is it you I have to thank for this?

KAJA: No, no, please don't think that.

SOLNESS: So you want to get married now.

KAJA (*quietly*): Ragnar and I have been engaged for nearly five years, so—

SOLNESS: So you think it's time something happened. That's it, isn't it?

KAJA: Ragnar and Uncle say I must. So I suppose I shall.

SOLNESS (*more gently*): You're quite fond of Ragnar too, aren't you, Kaja?

KAJA: I was very fond of Ragnar. Before I came here.

SOLNESS: But not any longer?

KAJA (*passionately*): Oh, you know there's only one person now. There's no one else in all the world. I'll never be fond of anyone else.

SOLNESS: Yes, you say that. But you're going to leave me, all the same. Leave me here to put up with everything alone.

KAJA: But couldn't I stay here with you even if Ragnar—?

SOLNESS: No, no, that's quite impossible. If Ragnar leaves me and sets up on his own account, he'll want to have you with him.

KAJA: Oh, I don't feel I can leave you! I can't, possibly—I can't!

37

SOLNESS: Then try to get Ragnar to put these foolish ideas out of his head. Marry him as much as you like—(*Changes his tone*) Yes, yes, I mean, persuade him to stay on in this good position he's got with me. Because then I can keep you too, Kaja dear.

KAJA: Oh, yes, how wonderful! If only it could work out like that!

SOLNESS (*takes her face between his hands and whispers*): I can't be without you, you see. I must have you here with me, every day.

KAJA: God! Oh God!

SOLNESS (*kisses her hair*): Kaja, Kaja!

KAJA (*drops on her knees*): Oh, you're so kind to me! So wonderfully kind!

SOLNESS (*sharply*): Get up! Get up, for heaven's sake! I think I can hear someone.

He helps her up. She falters over towards the desk. MRS SOL-NESS comes in through the door on the right. She looks thin and haggard, but retains traces of former beauty. Fair hair hanging in ringlets. She is elegantly dressed, all in black. She speaks rather slowly and plaintively.

MRS SOLNESS (*in the doorway*): Halvard!

SOLNESS (*turns*): Oh, is it you, my dear?

MRS SOLNESS (*glances at* KAJA): I've come at an inconvenient moment, I see.

SOLNESS: Not at all. Miss Fosli is just writing a short letter for me.

MRS SOLNESS: So I see.

SOLNESS: What was it you wanted, Aline?

MRS SOLNESS: I only wanted to tell you that Dr Herdal is in the drawing room. Would you like to come in and join us, Halvard?

SOLNESS (*looks at her suspiciously*): Hm. Has he something special to say to me?

MRS SOLNESS: No, nothing special. He came to visit me, and he'd like to see you while he's here.

SOLNESS (*laughs quietly*): Yes, I'm sure he would. Well, ask him to wait a moment.

MRS SOLNESS: You'll come and talk to him later then?

SOLNESS: Perhaps. Later, my dear—later. In a little while.

MRS SOLNESS (*with another look at* KAJA): Yes, well, don't forget now, Halvard. (*Goes out, closing the door behind her*).

KAJA (*quietly*): Oh, God, oh, God—I'm sure she thinks something dreadful about me!

SOLNESS: Nonsense. Well, not more than usual, anyway. I think you'd better go now though, Kaja.

KAJA: Yes, yes, I *must* go now.

SOLNESS (*sternly*): And get this other thing settled for me. Do you hear?

KAJA: Oh God, if it were only up to me—

SOLNESS: I want it settled, do you hear? And by tomorrow.

KAJA: If there's no other way, I'll break it off with him.

SOLNESS: Break it off? Have you gone mad? Do you want to break it off?

KAJA: Yes—I'd rather that than—! I must—I must stay here with you! I can't leave you! I can't—possibly!

SOLNESS: But for Christ's sake, what about Ragnar?

KAJA: Is it Ragnar you—?

SOLNESS: Oh no, no, of course not. You don't understand me. (*Gently, quietly*) Of course it's you I want, Kaja. Above all else. And it's just because of that that you must persuade Ragnar to stay. Now then, run along home.

KAJA: Yes, yes. Good night, then.

SOLNESS: Good night. (*As she turns to go*) Oh, by the way— are Ragnar's drawings in there?

KAJA: Yes, I didn't see him take them.

SOLNESS: Go in and find them for me. I might have a glance at them after all.

KAJA (*happily*): Oh, yes, please do.

SOLNESS: I'll do it for your sake, Kaja. Well, hurry up and find them for me, then!

KAJA *runs into the drawing office, searches anxiously in the drawer of the desk, finds a portfolio and brings it out.*

39

KAJA: All the drawings are here.

SOLNESS: Good. Put them over there on the table.

KAJA (*puts down the portfolio*): Good night, then. (*Pleadingly*) Think kindly of me, won't you?

SOLNESS: I always do. Good night, my dear little Kaja. (*Glances right*) Hurry up, now, run off.

MRS SOLNESS *and* DR HERDAL *enter through the door on the right. He is a stout, elderly man with a round, genial face, clean-shaven, with sparse, fair hair and gold-rimmed spectacles.*

MRS SOLNESS (*in the doorway*): Halvard, I couldn't keep the doctor waiting any longer.

SOLNESS: Well, come in, then.

MRS SOLNESS (*to* KAJA, *who is turning down the lamp on the desk*): Quite finished your letter, Miss Fosli?

KAJA (*confused*): Letter?

SOLNESS: Yes, it was just a short one.

MRS SOLNESS: It must have been very short.

SOLNESS: You may go, Miss Fosli. Be sure you're here punctually tomorrow.

KAJA: Why, of course. Good night, Mrs Solness. (*Goes out through hall door*).

MRS SOLNESS: You must be very pleased, Halvard, to have got hold of this young lady.

SOLNESS: Yes, indeed. She's useful in all sorts of ways.

MRS SOLNESS: I'm sure she is.

HERDAL: Good at book-keeping too?

SOLNESS: Well—she's picked up a little in these two years. And she's always cheerful and willing, whatever one asks her to do.

MRS SOLNESS: Yes, that must be a great advantage—

SOLNESS: It is. Especially when one isn't used to that kind of thing.

MRS SOLNESS (*gently reproachful*): Halvard, how can you say that?

SOLNESS: Oh no, no, Aline dear. I apologize.

MRS SOLNESS: There's no need. Well, Doctor, you'll come back later and take tea with us?

HERDAL: As soon as I've seen that patient, I'll be back.
MRS SOLNESS: Good. (*Goes out through door, right*).
SOLNESS: Are you in a hurry, Doctor?
HERDAL: No, not at all.
SOLNESS: May I have a word with you?
HERDAL: By all means.
SOLNESS: Let's sit down, then.

He indicates the rocking chair to the doctor, and seats himself in the armchair.

SOLNESS (*looks searchingly at him*): Tell me—did you notice anything about Aline?
HERDAL: Just now, you mean?
SOLNESS: Yes. In her attitude towards me. Did you notice anything?
HERDAL (*smiles*): Yes, well, damn it—one couldn't very well help noticing that your wife—er—
SOLNESS: Yes?
HERDAL: That your wife doesn't altogether approve of this Miss Fosli.
SOLNESS: Oh that? I'd noticed that myself.
HERDAL: Well, it's not really surprising, is it?
SOLNESS: What isn't?
HERDAL: That she doesn't exactly like your having another woman with you in the house every day.
SOLNESS: No, no, you may be right. But there's nothing to be done about that.
HERDAL: Couldn't you get yourself a male clerk?
SOLNESS: The first man-jack who put his head through the door? No, thank you, that's not the way I work.
HERDAL: But if your wife—? She's very frail, you know. If she can't stand this arrangement—
SOLNESS: Well, she'll have to put up with it. I don't mean it like that, but I have to keep Kaja Fosli. She's the only one who'll do.
HERDAL: The only one?
SOLNESS (*curtly*): Yes, the only one.

HERDAL (*pushes his chair closer*): Listen, Mr Solness. May I ask you a question—in strict confidence?

SOLNESS: By all means?

HERDAL: Women, you know—they've a damnably sharp nose for some things—

SOLNESS: They have. That's quite true. But—

HERDAL: Well, now, listen a moment. If your wife can't stand the sight of this Kaja Fosli—

SOLNESS: Yes, what then?

HERDAL: Isn't it possible that she may have some—some grounds for this instinctive dislike?

SOLNESS (*looks at him, and get up*): Oh-ho!

HERDAL: Please don't take this amiss. But am I right?

SOLNESS (*curtly, firmly*): No.

HERDAL: No grounds whatever?

SOLNESS: None other than her own suspiciousness.

HERDAL: You've—known a few women in your time.

SOLNESS: I have.

HERDAL: And been fairly fond of one or two of them?

SOLNESS: Oh, yes, that too.

HERDAL: But this Miss Fosli—there's nothing like that between you?

SOLNESS: Nothing whatever. As far as I'm concerned.

HERDAL: And what about her?

SOLNESS: I don't think you have a right to ask that, Doctor.

HERDAL: We were talking about your wife's instinct, remember.

SOLNESS: So we were. Well, as a matter of fact—(*lowers his voice*)—that sharp nose of Aline's that you were talking about hasn't altogether misled her.

HERDAL: Well—there we are!

SOLNESS (*sits*): Dr Herdal—I'm going to tell you a strange story. If you care to listen to it.

HERDAL: I like listening to strange stories.

SOLNESS: Good. Well, you remember, I dare say, some time ago I took Knut Brovik and his son into my employ—when things were going badly for the old man.

HERDAL: Yes, I know something about that.

SOLNESS: They're clever fellows, you know, those two.

They've both got ability, in different ways. But then the son went and got himself engaged; and then, of course, he wanted to marry the girl, and start out on his own. That's what they all want nowadays, these young people.

HERDAL (*laughs*): Yes, they've all got this bad habit of wanting to get married.

SOLNESS: Mm. Well, I didn't like it. I needed Ragnar. And the old man too. He's so damned clever at working out stresses and cubic content and all that bloody nonsense, you know.

HERDAL: Ah, well, that's part of the job, I suppose.

SOLNESS: So it is. But Ragnar—he wanted to go off and start on his own. He wouldn't listen to me.

HERDAL: But he's stayed with you.

SOLNESS: Well, that's just it. One day this girl, Kaja Fosli, came to see them on some errand or other. She'd never been here before. Well, when I saw how infatuated they were with each other, the idea struck me that if I could get her to come and work here in the office, Ragnar might stay too.

HERDAL: A reasonable supposition.

SOLNESS: Yes, but I didn't mention a word of all this. I just stood and looked at her—and kept wishing from the bottom of my heart that I had her here. Well, I chatted to her in a friendly way about one thing and another. And then she went.

HERDAL: Well?

SOLNESS: But the next day, in the evening, after old Brovik and Ragnar had gone home, she came back and acted just as though we'd come to some kind of an agreement.

HERDAL: What kind of agreement?

SOLNESS: The very one I'd been wanting to suggest. But which I hadn't mentioned a word about.

HERDAL: That was very strange.

SOLNESS: Yes. And now she wanted to know what kind of work she'd be doing. Whether she could begin at once the next morning. And so on.

HERDAL: Don't you think she did this to be near her young man?

SOLNESS: That was what I thought at first. But no, that wasn't it. She seemed to drift away from him—once she was here with me.

HERDAL: Drifted—over to you?

SOLNESS: Yes, completely. I've noticed that she knows I'm looking at her, even when her back's turned. She trembles and shivers if I even go near her. What do you make of that?

HERDAL: I suppose that could be explained.

SOLNESS: But what about this other business—that she thought I'd told her what I'd only wished for? Silently; inwardly, secretly. What do you make of that? Can you explain such a thing to me, Dr Herdal?

HERDAL: No, that's outside my field.

SOLNESS: That's what I thought; and that's why I haven't wanted to talk to you about it before. But in the long run, it's been a confounded nuisance to me, you know. I have to walk round here day after day pretending I— And it's not fair to her, poor girl. (*Violently*) But what else can I do? If she leaves me, Ragnar will go too.

HERDAL: And you haven't told your wife all this?

SOLNESS: No.

HERDAL: Why on earth don't you, then?

SOLNESS: Because somehow I feel it does me good to suffer Aline to do me an injustice.

HERDAL (*shakes his head*): I'm damned if I understand a word of that.

SOLNESS: Oh, yes. You see it's like paying a minute instalment on a great debt—a debt so vast it can never be settled.

HERDAL: A debt to your wife?

SOLNESS: Yes. And that—eases my mind a little. I can breathe more freely—for a while, you understand.

HERDAL: No, I'm damned if I understand a word—

SOLNESS (*breaks off and gets up again*): No, no—well, we won't talk about it any more. (*Wanders across the room, comes back and stops beside the table. He looks at the doctor with a quiet smile*) I suppose you think you're drawing me out pretty successfully, eh, Doctor?

44

HERDAL (*somewhat vexed*): Drawing you out? I really don't know what you mean, Mr Solness.

SOLNESS: Oh, stop pretending. I've noticed it clearly enough.

HERDAL: Noticed what?

SOLNESS: That you come here to keep an eye on me.

HERDAL: *I*? Why on earth should I do that?

SOLNESS: Because you think I'm—(*Flares up*) Damn it— you think the same about me as Aline does!

HERDAL: And what does she think about you?

SOLNESS (*in control of himself again*): She's begun to think I'm —well—you know—ill.

HERDAL: Ill? You? She's never mentioned a word about this to me. What could be the matter with you, my dear fellow?

SOLNESS (*leans over the back of the chair, and whispers*): Aline thinks I'm mad. Oh yes, she does.

HERDAL (*gets up*): But, my dear Mr Solness—

SOLNESS: Yes, by God, she does! That's what she thinks; and she's got you to believe it too! Oh, I know it, Doctor, I can see it in your behaviour. I'm not that easily deceived, I promise you.

HERDAL (*stares amazed*): Never, Mr Solness—never has such a thought entered my head.

SOLNESS (*with a distrustful smile*): Indeed? Hasn't it really?

HERDAL: Never. Nor your wife's either—I think I could swear to that.

SOLNESS: Well, I wouldn't if I were you. In a way, you see, she might not be altogether wrong.

HERDAL: No, really, this is going too far!

SOLNESS: Well, well, my dear Doctor—let's not pursue the matter. It's better left as it is. (*Quietly gleeful*) But now, listen, Doctor—hm—

HERDAL: Yes?

SOLNESS: As you don't think I'm—hm—ill—deranged—mad —or anything like that—

HERDAL: Well? What do you mean?

SOLNESS: Then you must be labouring under the illusion that I am an exceedingly lucky man.

HERDAL: Would that be an illusion?

SOLNESS (*laughs*): No, no—of course not! God forbid! Just think—to be a master builder, *the* master builder, Halvard Solness! Oh, yes, that's not to be sniffed at.

HERDAL: Yes, I really must say you seem to have been unbelievably lucky all your life.

SOLNESS (*represses an ironic smile*): That's right. I can't complain.

HERDAL: First of all that crazy old castle of yours burned down. And you'll admit that was a great stroke of luck.

SOLNESS: It was Aline's ancestral home. Remember that.

HERDAL: Yes, it must have been a terrible blow to her.

SOLNESS: She has never got over it, to this day. Not in all these twelve—thirteen—years.

HERDAL: What followed must have been the heaviest blow for her.

SOLNESS: The one with the other.

HERDAL: But it was that that gave you your start. You began as a poor country lad, and here you are, the top man in your profession. Oh, yes, Mr Solness, you've had the luck on your side all right.

SOLNESS (*glances nervously at him*): I know. That's what makes me so afraid.

HERDAL: Afraid? Because you've been lucky?

SOLNESS: Day and night—I'm afraid. Because some time my luck must change.

HERDAL: Nonsense. What should make it change?

SOLNESS (*swiftly, with conviction*): Youth.

HERDAL: Rubbish! Youth? You're not past it yet. On no—your position's stronger now than it's ever been.

SOLNESS: My luck will change. I know it. And I feel it will happen soon. Someone will stand up and demand: "Make way for me!" And then all the others will storm after him shaking their fists and shouting: "Make way! Make way!" Just you wait, Doctor. One fine day, youth will come and bang on that door—

HERDAL (*laughs*): Well, for heaven's sake, what of it?

46

SOLNESS: What of it? Why, that will be the end for master builder Solness.

There is a banging on the door to the left.

SOLNESS (*starts*): What was that? Did you hear something?
HERDAL: It's someone banging on the door.
SOLNESS (*loudly*): Come in!

HILDE WANGEL *comes in through the hall door. She is of medium height and slender and supple build. A little sun-tanned. She is wearing walking clothes, with a caught-up skirt, an open sailor collar and a small sailor hat on her head. She has a rucksack on her back, a plaid in a strap and a long alpenstock.*

HILDE (*goes over to* SOLNESS, *her eyes alight and happy*): Good evening!
SOLNESS (*looks at her uncertainly*): Good evening.
HILDE (*laughs*): I believe you don't recognize me.
SOLNESS: No—to be honest, just for a moment I—
HERDAL (*goes closer to her*): But I recognize you, Miss—
HILDE (*delighted*): Oh, no! Is it you?
HERDAL: Indeed it's me. (*To* SOLNESS) We met up in one of the mountain huts this summer. (*To* HILDE) What happened to the other ladies?
HILDE: Oh, they went on to the west coast.
HERDAL: They didn't like all that noise in the evenings.
HILDE: No, they didn't.
HERDAL (*wags his finger*): And you must confess you flirted a little with us!
HILDE: Well, it was more fun than knitting socks with all those old ladies.
HERDAL (*laughs*): I quite agree with you.
SOLNESS: Did you come to town this evening?
HILDE: Yes, I've just arrived.
HERDAL: All alone, Miss Wangel?
HILDE: Why, yes!
SOLNESS: Wangel? Is your name Wangel?
HILDE (*looks at him in merry surprise*): Yes, of course.

SOLNESS: Then—could it be that you are the daughter of the district physician up at Lysanger?

HILDE (*in the same tone as before*): Yes, who else would I be the daughter of?

SOLNESS: Oh, then we must have met up there. That summer when I went up to build the tower on the old church.

HILDE (*more earnestly*): Yes, that was it.

SOLNESS: Well, that's a long time ago.

HILDE (*gazes hard at him*): It was exactly ten years ago.

SOLNESS: You can only have been a child at the time.

HILDE (*carelessly*): I was nearly thirteen.

HERDAL: Is this the first time you've visited this town, Miss Wangel?

HILDE: Yes.

SOLNESS: So you—don't know anyone here, I suppose?

HILDE: No one except you. Oh, and your wife.

SOLNESS: Really? You know her too?

HILDE: Only slightly. We stayed in the same place up in the mountains. For a few days.

SOLNESS: Oh, up there.

HILDE: She said I might visit her if I ever came this way. (*Smiles*) Not that there was any need.

SOLNESS: I wonder why she didn't mention it to me—

HILDE *puts down her alpenstock by the stove, takes off her rucksack and puts it and her plaid on the sofa.* DR HERDAL *tries to help her;* SOLNESS *stands looking at her.*

HILDE (*goes towards him*): Can I stay the night here?

SOLNESS: I think that could be arranged.

HILDE: I haven't any clothes apart from what I'm wearing, you see. Oh, and a set of underclothes in my rucksack. I'll have to get them washed, though. They're filthy.

SOLNESS: Oh, well, that can be taken care of. I'd better tell my wife—

HERDAL: And I'll go and see my patient.

SOLNESS: Yes, do. And come back when you've finished.

HERDAL (*merrily, with a glance at* HILDE): Yes, you can be

48

damn sure I will! (*Laughs*) Well, you're a true prophet after all, Mr Solness.

SOLNESS: How do you mean?

HERDAL: Why, youth *has* come and banged on your door.

SOLNESS (*cheerfully*): Yes, but not quite the way I meant.

HERDAL: I should say not.

He goes out through the hall door. SOLNESS *opens the door to the right and speaks into the side room.*

SOLNESS: Aline! Will you come in here, please? There's a Miss Wangel here, whom you know.

MRS SOLNESS (*appears in the doorway*): Who is it, do you say? (*Sees* HILDE) Oh, is it you, my dear? (*Goes over to her and holds out her hand*) So you came this way after all?

SOLNESS: Miss Wangel has just arrived. She asks if she may stay the night.

MRS SOLNESS: With us? Yes, with pleasure.

SOLNESS: You know, to get her clothes in order.

MRS SOLNESS: I'll look after you as well as I can. It's my simple duty. Your luggage will be coming on later, of course?

HILDE: I haven't any.

MRS SOLNESS: Oh. Well, I'm sure you'll manage. Just make yourself at home with my husband while I get a room ready for you.

SOLNESS: Can't we use one of the nurseries? They're all ready.

MRS SOLNESS: Oh, yes. We've plenty of room *there*. (*To* HILDE) Sit down now, and rest a little.

She goes out to the right. HILDE *wanders round the room with her hands behind her back, looking at this and that.* SOLNESS *stands by the table downstage, also with his hands behind his back, watching her.*

HILDE (*stops and looks at him*): Have you got more than one nursery, then?

SOLNESS: There are three nurseries in this house.

HILDE: That's a lot. You must have heaps of children.

D

SOLNESS: No. We have no children. But now you can be the child here for a while.

HILDE: For tonight, yes. I won't cry. I intend to sleep like a log.

SOLNESS: Yes, I suppose you must be very tired.

HILDE: Not me! I'll sleep all right, though. I think it's absolutely marvellous to lie in bed and dream.

SOLNESS: Do you often dream at night?

HILDE: Gosh, yes. Nearly every night.

SOLNESS: What do you mostly dream about?

HILDE: I shan't tell you tonight. Some other time—perhaps.

She wanders across the room again, stops by the desk, and fingers among the books and papers.

SOLNESS (*goes over to her*): Are you looking for something?

HILDE: No, I'm just looking around. (*Turns*) Perhaps I mustn't?

SOLNESS: No, please do.

HILDE: Do you write in this big ledger?

SOLNESS: No, my book-keeper does. I leave that to her.

HILDE: A woman?

SOLNESS (*smiles*): Yes.

HILDE: And she works here with you?

SOLNESS: Yes.

HILDE: Is it a married woman?

SOLNESS: No, it isn't.

HILDE: I see.

SOLNESS: But she's going to get married soon.

HILDE: How very nice for her.

SOLNESS: But not so nice for me. Because then I'll have no-one to help me.

HILDE: Can't you find another one who'd do as well?

SOLNESS: Perhaps you'd like to stay here and—and write in the ledger?

HILDE (*looks at him scornfully*): What an idea! No, thank you. None of that.

She wanders across the room again and sits in the rocking chair. SOLNESS comes to the table beside her.

HILDE (*as though continuing*): There are better things here for me to do than that. (*Looks at him with a smile*) Don't you think so?

SOLNESS: I understand. You want to go shopping and get yourself something smart to wear.

HILDE (*gaily*): No, I think I'll give that a miss.

SOLNESS: Oh?

HILDE: I've spent all my money, you see.

SOLNESS (*laughs*): No luggage, and no money!

HILDE: No. Oh, hell, what do I care?

SOLNESS: You know, I like you for that.

HILDE: Just for that?

SOLNESS: Among other things. (*Sits in the armchair*) Is your father still alive?

HILDE: Yes, he's alive.

SOLNESS: And now you're thinking of studying here, perhaps?

HILDE: No, I hadn't thought of that.

SOLNESS: But you'll be staying for some time?

HILDE: That depends.

She sits for a few moments rocking herself and looking at him with a half smile. Then she takes off her hat and puts it on the table in front of her.

Mr Solness?

SOLNESS: Yes?

HILDE: Have you a bad memory?

SOLNESS: A bad memory? No, not that I'm aware of.

HILDE: Don't you want to talk to me about what happened up there?

SOLNESS (*starts, momentarily*) Up at Lysanger? (*Casually*) Well, there isn't much to talk about, is there?

HILDE (*looks at him reproachfully*): How can you say such a thing?

SOLNESS: All right, you talk to me about it, then.

HILDE: The day the tower was ready was a great day for our little town.

SOLNESS: Yes, I shan't forget that day in a hurry.

HILDE (*smiles*): Won't you? That's nice of you.

SOLNESS: Nice?

HILDE: There was music in the churchyard. And hundreds and hundreds of people. We schoolgirls were dressed in white. And we all had flags.

SOLNESS: Ah, yes. Those flags! I remember them.

HILDE: Then you climbed up the scaffolding. Up to the very top. You carried a big wreath with you. And you hung that wreath right up on the weathercock.

SOLNESS (*curtly, interrupting her*): I used to do that in those days. It's an old custom.

HILDE: It was so marvellously exciting to stand down there and stare up at you. Think—if he should fall now! The great master builder himself!

SOLNESS (*as though trying to deflect her train of thought*): Yes, yes, and it could very easily have happened. One of those little white devils suddenly waved and shouted up at me—

HILDE (*glowing and excited*): "Hurrah for Solness! Hurrah for the master builder!" Yes!

SOLNESS: And waved her flag and swung it about so that I— I amost turned giddy watching it.

HILDE (*quiet, serious*): That little devil was me.

SOLNESS (*stares hard at her*): Of course. It must have been you.

HILDE (*full of life again*): It was so frightfully exciting and marvellous! I'd never imagined there could be a master builder anywhere in the world who could build such an enormously high tower! And then to see you standing there yourself, right up at the top! And you weren't at all giddy. That was the thing that—that made me feel giddy.

SOLNESS: What made you so sure I wasn't—?

HILDE: Don't be silly! I knew it—in here. Otherwise, how could you have stood up there singing?

SOLNESS (*stares at her, amazed*): Singing? Did I sing?

HILDE: You certainly did.

SOLNESS (*shakes his head*): I've never sung a note in my life.

HILDE: Well, you sang then. It sounded like harps in the air.

SOLNESS (*thoughtfully*): This is most extraordinary.

HILDE (*looks at him silently for a moment, then says softly*):
But it was afterwards that the real thing happened.

SOLNESS: The real thing?

HILDE: Yes. I don't have to remind you about that?

SOLNESS: Yes, remind me a little about that, too.

HILDE: Don't you remember they gave a great banquet for
you at the Club?

SOLNESS: Oh yes. That must have been the same evening. I
left next morning.

HILDE: When it ended we invited you home for supper.

SOLNESS: You're quite right, Miss Wangel. It's remarkable
how clearly you remember all these little details.

HILDE: Little details! You're a fine one! Was it just a little
detail that I happened to be alone in the room when you
came in?

SOLNESS: Were you?

HILDE: You didn't call me a little devil then.

SOLNESS: No, I don't suppose I did.

HILDE: You said I looked beautiful in my white dress. Like
a little princess.

SOLNESS: So you did, Miss Wangel. And besides—I felt so
happy and free that evening—

HILDE: And then you said that when I grew up, I would be
your princess.

SOLNESS (*with a short laugh*): Well, well! Did I say that,
too?

HILDE: Yes, you did. And then, when I asked how long I
should have to wait, you said you'd come back in ten years
—like a troll—and carry me off. To Spain or somewhere
like that. And you promised that when we got there, you'd
buy me a kingdom.

SOLNESS (*in the same tone as before*): Yes, after a good dinner
one doesn't count the shillings. But did I really say all
this?

HILDE (*laughs quietly*): Yes. And you told me what this
kingdom was to be called, too.

SOLNESS: Oh, what?

HILDE: You said it was to be called Orangia.

SOLNESS: Well, that's a nice appetizing name.

HILDE: I didn't like it. It sounded as though you were making fun of me.

SOLNESS: I'm sure I didn't mean that.

HILDE: I can well believe you didn't. Considering what you did next—

SOLNESS: And what on earth did I do next?

HILDE: No, that's the last straw! Have you forgotten that, too? I really think you might have remembered that.

SOLNESS: Well, give me a hint, and perhaps— Well?

HILDE: You took me in your arms and kissed me, Mr Solness.

SOLNESS (*gets up from his chair, his mouth open*): *I* did?

HILDE: Yes, you did. You took me in both your arms and bent me backwards and kissed me. Many, many times.

SOLNESS: Oh, but my dear, good Miss Wangel—

HILDE (*gets up*): You're not going to deny it?

SOLNESS: I certainly am!

HILDE (*looks at him scornfully*): Oh. I see.

She turns and walks slowly across to near the stove, where she stands motionless with her back towards him and her hands behind her. Short pause.

SOLNESS (*goes diffidently up behind her*): Miss Wangel—!

HILDE *remains silent and motionless.*

SOLNESS: Don't stand there like a statue. All this that you've just told me must have been something you've dreamed. (*He touches her arm*) Now, listen—

HILDE *makes an impatient gesture with her arm.*

SOLNESS (*as a thought strikes him*): Or—wait a moment! No, there's more to it than that.

HILDE *does not move.*

SOLNESS (*speaks softly, but with emphasis*): I must have thought all this. I must have wanted it—wished it—desired it. So that— Couldn't that be an explanation?

HILDE *remains silent.*

SOLNESS (*bursts out impatiently*): Oh, damn it. Have it your own way—say I *did* it!

54

HILDE (*turns her head slightly, but does not look at him*): You confess?

SOLNESS: Yes. Anything you say.

HILDE: That you put your arms around me?

SOLNESS: Yes, yes.

HILDE: And bent me over backwards?

SOLNESS: Yes, right back.

HILDE: And kissed me?

SOLNESS: Yes, I kissed you.

HILDE: Many times?

SOLNESS: As many as you like.

HILDE (*turns quickly towards him, her eyes again glowing and excited*): You see! I wormed it out of you in the end!

SOLNESS (*smiles wryly*): Yes, just fancy—that I could forget a thing like that!

HILDE (*walks away from him, a little sulky again*): Oh, you've kissed so many women in your time, I suppose.

SOLNESS: No, you mustn't think I'm that sort.

HILDE *sits in the armchair.* SOLNESS *stands, leaning against the rocking chair.*

SOLNESS (*looks searchingly at her*): Miss Wangel?

HILDE: Yes?

SOLNESS: What happened? What more happened between you and me?

HILDE: Nothing more happened. You know that. The other guests arrived, and then—well—

SOLNESS: Yes, of course! The others arrived, and—fancy my forgetting that too!

HILDE: Oh, you haven't forgotten anything. You're just a bit ashamed. One doesn't forget things like that. I know.

SOLNESS: No, one would think not.

HILDE (*alive again, looks at him*): Perhaps you've also forgotten what day it was.

SOLNESS: What day?

HILDE: Yes, what day was it when you hung the wreath on the tower? Well? Tell me! At once!

SOLNESS: Hm—I've forgotten the actual day, I must confess.

55

I know it was ten years ago. Some time in the autumn.

HILDE (*nods slowly several times*): It was ten years ago. The nineteenth of September.

SOLNESS: Yes, about then, I suppose. So you remember that, too! (*Pause*) But wait a moment—! Today is the nineteenth of September!

HILDE: Exactly. And the ten years are up. And you didn't come—as you'd promised you would.

SOLNESS: Promised? I only said it to frighten you.

HILDE: I didn't find it frightening.

SOLNESS: Well, to tease you.

HILDE: Was that all you wanted to do? Tease me?

SOLNESS: Oh, I don't remember—for fun, if you like. It can't have been anything else, you were only a child at the time.

HILDE: Oh, maybe I wasn't such a child. Not such a little innocent as you think.

SOLNESS (*looks searchingly at her*): Did you really and seriously think I'd come back?

HILDE (*suppressing a half-teasing smile*): Oh, yes! I'd expected no less of you.

SOLNESS: That I'd come to your home and take you away with me?

HILDE: Yes. Like a troll.

SOLNESS: And make you a princess?

HILDE: That's what you promised.

SOLNESS: And give you a kingdom, too?

HILDE (*looks up at the ceiling*): Why not? It didn't have to be an ordinary kingdom.

SOLNESS: But—something else, just as good?

HILDE: Yes, at least as good. (*Looks at him for a moment*) If you could build the highest church tower in the world, I thought you would be able to find your way to a kingdom too. Of some kind.

SOLNESS (*shakes his head*): I can't quite make you out, Miss Wangel.

HILDE: You can't? To me it's all so simple.

SOLNESS: No, I can't make out whether you mean what you say. Or whether you're simply having me on—

HILDE (*smiles*): Making fun of you?

SOLNESS: Yes, exactly. Making fun of me. Of us both. (*Looks at her*) Have you known for long that I'm married?

HILDE: I've known all along. Why do you ask that?

SOLNESS (*casually*): No, no, I just wondered. (*Looks earnestly at her and says quietly*): Why have you come?

HILDE: Because I want my kingdom. The time's up now.

SOLNESS (*laughs involuntarily*): That's a good one!

HILDE (*merrily*): Stump up my kingdom, master builder! (*Taps with her finger*) On the table!

SOLNESS (*pushes the rocking chair closer, and sits down*): Seriously, why have you come? What do you want here?

HILDE: Well, to begin with, I want to go round and look at everything you've built.

SOLNESS: Then you'll have a lot of walking to do.

HILDE: Yes, you've built such a frightful lot.

SOLNESS: I have. Especially these last years.

HILDE: Lots of church spires too? As high as the sky?

SOLNESS: No. I don't build church spires any more. Nor churches, neither.

HILDE: What do you build now, then?

SOLNESS: Homes for people to live in.

HILDE (*thoughtfully*): Couldn't you put little spires on them, too?

SOLNESS (*starts*): What do you mean?

HILDE: I mean—something that points—straight up in the air. With a weathercock high up at the top—so high it makes you giddy!

SOLNESS (*musingly*): It's strange you should say that. That's just what I'd like to do—most of all.

HILDE (*impatiently*): Why don't you, then?

SOLNESS (*shakes his head*): No, people don't want that.

HILDE: Really? They don't want that?

SOLNESS (*more lightly*): But now I'm building a new home for myself. Here, just opposite.

HILDE: For yourself?

SOLNESS: Yes. It's almost ready. And on that there's a spire.

HILDE: A high spire?

57

SOLNESS: Yes.

HILDE: Very high?

SOLNESS: People are sure to say it's too high. For a home.

HILDE: I'm going out to see that spire first thing tomorrow morning.

SOLNESS (*sits leaning his cheek on his hand, staring at her*): Tell me, Miss Wangel, what's your name? Your first name, I mean?

HILDE: Hilde, of course.

SOLNESS (*as before*): Hilde? Really?

HILDE: Don't you remember? You called me Hilde. The day you misbehaved.

SOLNESS: I called you Hilde?

HILDE: Yes, but then you said "little Hilde". And I didn't like that.

SOLNESS: So you didn't like that, Miss Hilde?

HILDE: No. Not just then. But—Princess Hilde—that'll sound quite nice. I think.

SOLNESS: Yes, indeed. Princess Hilde of—what was our kingdom to be called?

HILDE: Ugh! I don't wany any of that stupid kingdom. I want a quite different kind of kingdom.

SOLNESS (*has leant back in his chair, still staring at her*): Isn't it strange—? The more I think about it now—the more it seems to me as though for years I've been torturing myself—hm—

HILDE: Go on.

SOLNESS: Trying to remember something—something that had happened to me, and that I must have forgotten. But I could never discover what it was.

HILDE: You ought to have tied a knot in your handkerchief, master builder.

SOLNESS: Then I'd only have gone round wondering what the knot stood for.

HILDE: Oh, well. I suppose it takes trolls like you to make a world.

SOLNESS (*gets up slowly*): I'm glad you've come to me just at this time.

HILDE (*looks into his eyes*): Are you glad?

SOLNESS: I've been so alone. Staring at it all. So helpless. (*Lowers his voice*) You see—I've begun to be so afraid—so terribly afraid—of youth.

HILDE (*scornfully*): Youth? Is youth something to be afraid off?

SOLNESS: Yes, it is. That's why I've shut myself up here. (*Secretively*) Some day, youth will come here and thunder on my door, and force its way in to me.

HILDE: Then I think you ought to go out and open the door.

SOLNESS: Open the door?

HILDE: Yes. And let youth in. As a friend.

SOLNESS: No, no! Youth means retribution. It marches at the head of a rebel army. Under a new banner.

HILDE (*gets up, looks at him and says, her mouth trembling*): Can you use me, master builder?

SOLNESS: Yes! Yes, now I can use you! For you, too, march under a new banner. Youth against youth—!

DR HERDAL *comes in through the hall door.*

HERDAL: Hullo! Are you and our young friend still here?

SOLNESS: Yes. We two have found many things to talk about.

HILDE: Both old and new.

HERDAL: Oh, have you indeed!

HILDE: It's been great fun. The master builder has a quite incredible memory. Every little detail—just like that!

MRS SOLNESS *enters through the door on the right.*

MRS SOLNESS: Well, Miss Wangel, your room's ready now.

HILDE: Oh, how kind you are!

SOLNESS (*to* MRS SOLNESS): The nursery?

MRS SOLNESS: Yes. The middle one. But let's have supper first.

SOLNESS (*nods to* HILDE): Hilde shall sleep in the nursery tonight.

MRS SOLNESS (*looks at him*): Hilde?

SOLNESS: Yes, Miss Wangel's name is Hilde. I used to know her when she was a child.

MRS SOLNESS: No, did you really, Halvard? Well, please come in. Supper's on the table.

She takes DR HERDAL'S *arm and goes out with him to the right. Meanwhile,* HILDE *has gathered her things together.*

HILDE (*swiftly, quietly, to* SOLNESS): Was it true, what you said? Can you find some use for me?

SOLNESS (*takes her things from her*): You are the one I've been wanting.

HILDE (*looks at him joyful and amazed, and clasps her hands*): Oh, master builder—!

SOLNESS (*tensely*): Yes?

HILDE: Then I have my kingdom!

SOLNESS (*involuntarily*): Hilde!

HILDE (*her mouth trembling again*): *Almost*—I was going to say.

She goes out right. SOLNESS *follows her.*

ACT TWO

A pleasantly furnished little sitting-room in SOLNESS'S *house. In the rear wall is a glass door leading to the verandah and garden. The right-hand corner is broken by a bay containing stands for plants and a large window. A similar bay in the left-hand corner contains a small door covered with wallpaper. In each of the side walls is an ordinary door. Downstage right, a console table with a large mirror. A rich profusion of flowers and plants. Downstage left, a sofa, with a table and chairs. Further back, a bookcase. In the middle of the room, in front of the bay, a small table and one or two chairs. It is early morning.*

SOLNESS *is seated at the small table, with* RAGNAR BROVIK'S *portfolio open in front of him. He leafs through the drawings, examining some of them closely.* MRS SOLNESS *is going round silently with a small can, watering the flowers. She is dressed in black, as before. Her hat, overcoat and parasol lie on a chair by the mirror.* SOLNESS *looks at her once or twice without her noticing. Neither of them speaks.* KAJA FOSLI *comes quietly in through the door on the left.*

SOLNESS (*turns his head and says casually*): Oh, it's you.

KAJA: I just wanted to tell you I'm here.

SOLNESS: Yes, good. Is Ragnar there, too?

KAJA: No, not yet. He had to stay behind to wait for the doctor. He won't be long, he wants to come and ask you how you feel about the—

SOLNESS: How's the old man feeling today?

KAJA: Bad. He says will you please excuse him, but he'll have to stay in bed today.

SOLNESS: By all means let him. You go along and start work, though.

61

KAJA: Yes. (*Stops at the door*) Perhaps you'd like to speak to Ragnar when he comes?

SOLNESS: No, not particularly.

KAJA *goes out again to the left.* SOLNESS *continues to look through the drawings.*

MRS SOLNESS (*over by the plants*): It wouldn't surprise me if he died too.

SOLNESS (*looks at her*): Too? Who else?

MRS SOLNESS (*not replying*): Yes, yes; old Brovik—he'll die too now, Halvard. You'll see.

SOLNESS: Aline dear, don't you think you should go out and get a little fresh air?

MRS SOLNESS: Yes, I should, shouldn't I? (*Continues attending to the flowers*).

SOLNESS (*bent over the drawings*): Is she still asleep?

MRS SOLNESS (*looks at him*): Is it Miss Wangel you're sitting there thinking about.

SOLNESS (*indifferently*): Just happened to think of her.

MRS SOLNESS: Miss Wangel's been up a long time.

SOLNESS: Oh, has she?

MRS SOLNESS: When I looked in she was seeing to her clothes.

(*She goes to the mirror and begins slowly to put on her hat*).

SOLNESS (*after a short pause*): Well, we've found a use for one of the nurseries after all, haven't we, Aline?

MRS SOLNESS: Yes, we have.

SOLNESS: I think that's better than that they should all stand empty.

MRS SOLNESS: Yes, that emptiness is horrible. You're right there.

SOLNESS (*closes the portfolio, gets up and goes over to her*): From now on things will be better, Aline. You'll see. Much more satisfactory. Life will be easier to bear. Especially for you.

MRS SOLNESS (*looks at him*): From now on?

SOLNESS: Yes, Aline, believe me—

MRS SOLNESS: You mean—because she's come?

SOLNESS (*controls himself*): I mean, of course, once we've moved into the new house.

MRS SOLNESS (*takes her overcoat*): Do you really think so, Halvard? Things will be better?

SOLNESS: I'm sure they will. You believe that too, don't you?

MRS SOLNESS: I don't believe anything where that new house is concerned.

SOLNESS (*vexed*): I'm sorry to hear that, my dear. It was mainly for your sake I built it. (*Tries to help her on with her coat*).

MRS SOLNESS (*moves away*): You do much too much for me.

SOLNESS (*almost violently*): No, no, you mustn't talk like that, Aline. I can't bear to hear you say such things.

MRX SOLNESS: Very well, Halvard, I won't say them.

SOLNESS: I'm right, though. You'll be happy in that new house. You'll see.

MRS SOLNESS: God! *I*—happy—?

SOLNESS: Yes! Yes! I promise you! Don't you see, there'll be so much there that'll remind you of your own home—

MRS SOLNESS: Father's and mother's home. And it was burnt. All burnt.

SOLNESS (*subdued*): Yes, my poor Aline. That was a terrible blow for you.

MRS SOLNESS: You can build as much as you like, Halvard— you'll never be able to build a real home for me again.

SOLNESS (*turns and walks away across the room*): Well, in that case for God's sake let's not talk about it any more.

MRS SOLNESS: Well, we don't usually talk about it, anyway. You always avoid the subject—

SOLNESS (*stops abruptly and looks at her*): *I* do? And why should I avoid the subject?

MRS SOLNESS: Oh, I understand you so well, Halvard. You want to spare me. And stop me feeling guilty. As far as you can.

SOLNESS (*stares amazed*): Stop *you* feeling guilty! Are you— are you talking about yourself, Aline?

MRS SOLNESS: Yes, who else would I be talking about?

SOLNESS (*involuntarily, to himself*): That too!

MRS SOLNESS: It's not so much what happened to the old house. I think I could resign myself to that. After all, that was an accident—

SOLNESS: Yes, you're right. Accidents will happen, and it's no use blaming oneself for them.

MRS SOLNESS: But the dreadful thing that happened after the fire. That's what I can't forget. I can't, I can't, I can't!

SOLNESS (*violently*): Don't think about it, Aline.

MRS SOLNESS: I have to think about it. And I must talk about it some time. I don't think I can endure it any longer. And I never *can* forgive myself—

SOLNESS: Forgive *yourself*—?

MRS SOLNESS: Yes—because I had a duty to all of you. To you, and the children. I should have hardened myself, I shouldn't have let fear weaken me. Or grief—for my burnt home. Oh, if only I'd had the strength, Halvard!

SOLNESS (*quiet, shaken, comes towards her*): Aline, you must promise me you'll never let these thoughts enter your head again. Promise me that, my dear.

MRS SOLNESS: God—promise, promise! It's easy to promise anything—

SOLNESS (*walks across the room*): Oh, this is hopeless, hopeless! Not a ray of light ever enters this home. Not a glimmer.

MRS SOLNESS: This is no home, Halvard.

SOLNESS: No, you're right. And, God knows, you may be right too when you say it won't be any better in the new house.

MRS SOLNESS: Never. It'll be just as empty and just as desolate there as it is here.

SOLNESS (*violently*): Why in God's name have we built it, then? Can you tell me that?

MRS SOLNESS: No. That you must answer yourself.

SOLNESS (*looks at her suspiciously*): What do you mean by that, Aline?

MRS SOLNESS: What do I mean?

SOLNESS: Yes, damn it! You said it so strangely. As though you meant something else.

MRS SOLNESS: No, I assure you—

SOLNESS (*goes closer*): Oh, thank you very much—I know what I know. I've got eyes and ears, Aline. You can be sure of that.

MRS SOLNESS: What do you mean? What do you mean?

SOLNESS (*stands in front of her*): You find some cunning, hidden meaning in every harmless little thing I say, don't you, eh?

MRS SOLNESS: I, Halvard. Do *I* do that?

SOLNESS (*laughs*): Oh, it's very understandable, Aline. When you've a sick man on your hands, well—

MRS SOLNESS (*alarmed*): Sick? Are you sick, Halvard.

SOLNESS: An idiot, then. A lunatic. Call me what you like.

MRS SOLNESS (*gropes for the back of the chair and sits down*): Halvard—for God's sake—!

SOLNESS: But you're wrong, both of you. You and your doctor. There's nothing the matter with me. (*He walks up and down the room. MRS SOLNESS watches him anxiously. At length he comes over to her, and says calmly*) There's nothing the matter with me at all.

MRS SOLNESS: No, of course not. But—what's worrying you, then?

SOLNESS: It's this dreadful burden of debt that's crushing me—

MRS SOLNESS: Debt? But you're not in debt to anyone, Halvard.

SOLNESS (*quietly*): I owe a boundless debt to you. To you, Aline.

MRS SOLNESS (*rises slowly*): What is behind all this?

SOLNESS: There's nothing *behind* it. I've never done you any harm. Not wittingly, anyway. And yet—it feels as though a huge stone of guilt lay on me, weighing me down, crushing me.

MRS SOLNESS: Guilt? Towards me, you mean?

SOLNESS: Towards you, most of all.

MRS SOLNESS: Then you really are—sick, Halvard.

SOLNESS: I suppose I must be. Sick—or something. (*Glances towards the door on the right, as it is opened*) Ah! Now it grows lighter!

E   65

HILDE WANGEL *enters. She has made one or two changes in her dress, and has let down her skirt so that it reaches to her ankles.*

HILDE: Good morning, master builder!

SOLNESS (*nods*): Slept well?

HILDE: Marvellously! Just as though I was in a cradle. Oh, I lay there and stretched myself like a—like a princess.

SOLNESS (*with a little smile*): Really comfortable?

HILDE: I should say so!

SOLNESS: And you dreamed too, I suppose?

HILDE: Yes. Ugh—beastly!

SOLNESS: Oh?

HILDE: Yes, I dreamed I'd fallen over a frightfully high, steep cliff. Do you ever have that dream?

SOLNESS: Er—yes—now and then—

HILDE: It's so exciting! As you fall and fall—

SOLNESS: It makes me go cold as ice.

HILDE: Do you hug your knees up under you as you fall?

SOLNESS: Yes, as high as I can.

HILDE: So do I.

MRS SOLNESS (*takes her parasol*): Well, I'd better be going into town now, Halvard. (*To* HILDE) I'll see if I can bring back one or two things you might need.

HILDE (*tries to embrace her*): Oh, darling, beautiful Mrs Solness! You're really too sweet. Frightfully sweet—

MRS SOLNESS (*freeing herself*): Not at all. It's my simple duty. And I'm only too glad to do it.

HILDE (*pouts, piqued*): Actually, I think I'm all right to go into town as I am, now that I've made myself smart. Or perhaps I'm not?

MRS SOLNESS: To speak frankly, I think one or two people might raise their eyebrows.

HILDE: Pooh! Is that all? That'd be rather a lark.

SOLNESS (*concealing his mood*): Yes, but people might think you were mad too, you see.

HILDE: Mad? Are there so many mad people in this town?

SOLNESS (*points to his forehead*): Here you see one, anyway.

HILDE: *You*—master builder?

MRS SOLNESS: Oh, but my dear Halvard, really!

SOLNESS: Haven't you noticed yet?

HILDE: No, I certainly haven't. (*Thinks and gives a little laugh*) Yes, perhaps in just one little thing, now I think of it.

SOLNESS: You hear that, Aline?

MRS SOLNESS: In what thing, Miss Wangel?

HILDE: No, I'm not telling.

SOLNESS: Yes, do tell us.

HILDE: No, thanks—I'm not *that* mad.

MRS SOLNESS: When you and Miss Wangel are alone, she'll tell you, Halvard.

SOLNESS: Oh, do you think so?

MRS SOLNESS: Why, yes. You and she have been such good friends; ever since she was a child, you say. (*She goes out through the door on the left*).

HILDE (*after a moment*): Do you think your wife doesn't like me?

SOLNESS: Why, did you notice anything?

HILDE: Didn't you?

SOLNESS (*avoiding the question*): Aline's become very shy of people these last years.

HILDE: That too?

SOLNESS: But if only you could get to know her properly—she's very good and kind—a really good woman—

HILDE (*impatiently*): If she is, why did she have to talk like that about duty?

SOLNESS: About duty?

HILDE: Yes, she said she'd go out and buy something for me because it was her duty. Oh, I can't stand that nasty beastly word.

SOLNESS: Why not?

HILDE: It sounds so cold and sharp, like a knife. Duty, duty, duty! Don't you feel that, too? That it—somehow—pierces you?

SOLNESS: Hm—I haven't given it much thought.

HILDE: Oh yes! And if she's as good and kind as you pretend, why should she say a thing like that?

SOLNESS: Well, good Lord, what should she have said?

HILDE: She could have said she wanted to do it because she liked me so much. Or something like that, she could have said. Something really warm and kind, don't you think?

SOLNESS (*looks at her*): So that's what you want?

HILDE: Yes. (*Walks round the room, stops in front of the bookcase and looks at the books*). You've an awful lot of books.

SOLNESS: Oh, I've collected a few.

HILDE: Do you read them all?

SOLNESS: I used to try. Do you read?

HILDE: No. Not any more. It all seems so meaningless.

SOLNESS: That's exactly how I feel.

HILDE *wanders round for a few moments, stops by the small table, opens the portfolio and glances through it.*

HILDE: Have you done all these drawings?

SOLNESS: No, a young man I have here to help me.

HILDE: A pupil of yours?

SOLNESS: Oh, yes, I dare say he's learned something from me, too.

HILDE (*sits*): He must be awfully clever, then. (*Looks at a drawing for a moment*) Isn't he?

SOLNESS: Oh, not so bad. For my purposes—

HILDE: Oh, *yes*. He must be frightfully clever.

SOLNESS: You can tell that from his drawings, can you?

HILDE: What, this stuff? Oh, no. But if he's been studying with *you*—

SOLNESS: Oh, that? There are plenty of people round here who've studied under me. And nothing's become of them.

HILDE (*looks at him and shakes her head*): Upon my soul, I don't understand how you can be so stupid.

SOLNESS: Stupid? Do you think I'm so very stupid, then?

HILDE: Yes, indeed I do. Letting these young men come here and pick your brains—

SOLNESS (*starts*): Well? And why not?

HILDE (*gets up, half in earnest, half laughing*): Oh, no, master builder, that's no good. No one but you should be allowed to build. Only you. Do it all yourself. Now you know.

68

SOLNESS (*unwillingly*): Hilde—

HILDE: Yes?

SOLNESS: What on earth made you say that?

HILDE: Why—*that's* not such a wicked idea, is it?

SOLNESS: No, I didn't mean that. But—I'll tell you something.

HILDE: Well, what?

SOLNESS: I walk up and down in this house—incessantly—
in silence—and loneliness—turning that very idea over in
my mind.

HILDE: Yes, well, that's very reasonable.

SOLNESS (*glances searchingly at her*): I dare say you've noticed
this?

HILDE: No, I haven't *noticed* anything.

SOLNESS: But just now—when you said you thought I was—
wrong in the head—on one point of the compass. Did
you mean—?

HILDE: Oh, I was thinking of something quite different then.

SOLNESS: What were you thinking of?

HILDE: Never you mind, master builder.

SOLNESS (*walks across the room*): As you please. (*Stops by
the bay*) Come here, and I'll show you something.

HILDE (*goes closer*): What is it?

SOLNESS (*points*): Just beyond that big stone-pit—

HILDE: That new house?

SOLNESS: That one that's being built, yes. Almost finished
now.

HILDE: It's got a very high tower, hasn't it?

SOLNESS: The scaffolding's still round it.

HILDE: Is that your new house?

SOLNESS: Yes.

HILDE: The house you're going to move into soon?

SOLNESS: Yes.

HILDE (*looks at him*): Are there nurseries in that house, too?

SOLNESS: Three, the same as here.

HILDE: And no children?

SOLNESS: There won't be any, either.

HILDE (*with a half-smile*): Well, wasn't I right?

SOLNESS: What do you mean?

69

HILDE: You are a little—mad—after all.

SOLNESS: Was *that* what you were thinking?

HILDE: Yes—all those empty nurseries, where I was sleeping.

SOLNESS (*quietly*): We have had children—Aline and I.

HILDE (*looks at him tensely*): Have you?

SOLNESS: Two little boys. Both the same age.

HILDE: Twins?

SOLNESS: Yes, twins. It's nearly twelve years ago, now.

HILDE (*gently*): You mean they're both—? You haven't got these twins any longer?

SOLNESS (*quiet, moved*): We only had them three weeks. Hardly that. (*Bursts out*) Oh, Hilde, I can't tell you how glad I am that you've come! Now at last I've found someone I can talk to.

HILDE: Can't you talk to—to her, too?

SOLNESS: Not about this. Not the way I want to—and need to. (*Sadly*) Nor about much else, either.

HILDE: Was that all you meant when you said you needed me?

SOLNESS: Must have been—I suppose. Yesterday, at least. Today, I'm no longer so sure. (*Breaks off; takes her by the hand and leads her to the sofa*) There. You can see the garden from there. (*She sits in the corner of the sofa. He brings a chair nearer to her*) Would you like to hear about it?

HILDE: Yes, I love sitting and listening to you.

SOLNESS (*sits*): Well, I'll tell you all about it.

HILDE: Now I can see you *and* the garden, master builder. Now then, tell me! Come on!

SOLNESS (*points through the bay window*): Up there—where you see that new house—

HILDE: Yes?

SOLNESS: That's where Aline and I lived during the first years of our marriage. In those days there used to be an old house up there which had belonged to her mother. She left it to us. And all the grounds with it.

HILDE: Was there a spire on that house, too?

SOLNESS: No, nothing of the kind. To look at from the outside, it was a great, dark ugly crate. But indoors it was nice and cosy enough.

HILDE: Did you pull the old thing down?

SOLNESS: No, It was burned down.

HILDE: The whole thing?

SOLNESS: Yes.

HILDE: Was that a terrible blow to you?

SOLNESS: It depends which way you look at it. It was that fire that made me a master builder.

HILDE: Oh? But—?

SOLNESS: Our two little boys had just been born—

HILDE: The poor little twins.

SOLNESS: They were so healthy and strong when they were born. And you could see them growing from day to day—

HILDE: Babies grow frightfully quickly the first few days.

SOLNESS: It was the prettiest sight you could wish to see, Aline lying there with the two of them. But then there came the night of the fire—

HILDE: What happened? Tell me! Was anyone burned alive?

SOLNESS: No, not that. Everyone got safely out of the house—

HILDE: Well, then, what—?

SOLNESS: It was a terrible shock for Aline. The alarm, and being rushed out of the house, into the ice-cold night— they had to be carried out, just as they were—she and the little boys.

HILDE: And they couldn't stand the cold?

SOLNESS: Oh, they stood up to that all right. But Aline caught a fever. And it infected her milk. She had to feed them herself. It was her duty, she said. And both our little boys—both of them—

HILDE: They didn't get over *that*?

SOLNESS: No, they didn't get over that. It—took them from us.

HILDE: That must have been a great loss for you.

SOLNESS: It was great enough for me. But ten times greater for her. (*Clenches his hands in quiet fury*) How can such a thing be allowed to happen in this world? (*Curtly*) From that day on, I lost interest in building churches.

71

HILDE: Then you didn't enjoy building the steeple on our church?

SOLNESS: I didn't. How relieved and glad I was when it was finished.

HILDE: I know that.

SOLNESS: And now I shall never build anything like that again. Neither churches, nor steeples.

HILDE (*nods slowly*): Just houses, for people to live in.

SOLNESS: Homes, Hilde. Homes for men and women and children.

HILDE: But homes with high towers and spires on top.

SOLNESS: Yes, if possible. (*Speaks more lightly*) Well, you see —as I said—that fire started me on my way. As a master builder.

HILDE: Why don't you call yourself an architect, like all the others?

SOLNESS: I've never really studied it properly. Most of what I know I've found out for myself.

HILDE: But you got to the top, master builder.

SOLNESS: Yes; fanned by those flames. I cut up nearly all the grounds into building plots. And *there* I was able to build, just the way I wanted. And from then on things went well for me.

HILDE (*looks searchingly at him*): You must be a very happy man, then. With all the success you've had.

SOLNESS: Happy? You say that, too. Like all the others.

HILDE: Yes, I think you should be. If you could only stop thinking about those two little boys—

SOLNESS (*slowly*): Those two little boys—are not so easy to forget, Hilde.

HILDE (*a little uncertain*): So they still stand in your way? After so many years?

SOLNESS (*stares at her, without replying*): A happy man, you said—

HILDE: Yes, well, aren't you—apart from this?

SOLNESS (*still staring at her*): When I told you about the fire—

HILDE: Go on.

SOLNESS: Didn't anything particular strike you?

HILDE: No. I can't think of anything.

SOLNESS: If it hadn't been for that fire, I wouldn't have been able to build homes. Bright, peaceful comfortable homes, where mothers and fathers could live with their children secure and happy in the knowledge that it is good to be alive. And, above all, to belong to each other—in great things and in small.

HILDE: Yes, doesn't it bring you great happiness to know that you can build such wonderful homes for them?

SOLNESS: But the price, Hilde. The terrible price I had to pay.

HILDE: Is there no way to put all that behind you?

SOLNESS: No. Because—to be able to build homes for other people, I had to renounce for ever all hope of having a home of my own. I mean a home with children. And for their father and mother.

HILDE: For ever, you say? Was that absolutely necessary?

SOLNESS (*nods slowly*): That was the price I had to pay for this "happiness" people talk so much about. (*Takes a deep breath*) That happiness—hm—that happiness wasn't to be had at a lesser price, Hilde.

HILDE: But perhaps things may still work out?

SOLNESS: No, they never can. Never. That is another consequence of the fire. And of Aline's illness which resulted from it.

HILDE (*looks at him with an enigmatic expression*): And yet you are building all these nurseries?

SOLNESS: Haven't you noticed, Hilde, that the impossible— beckons and calls to us?

HILDE (*thinks*): The impossible? (*Excitedly*) Why yes! Is it like that with you as well?

SOLNESS: It is.

HILDE: Then you have something of the troll in you, too.

SOLNESS: Why troll?

HILDE: Well, what would you call it?

SOLNESS (*gets up*): No, no, you may be right. (*Violently*) But please God I may never become a troll like the one who mocks me in everything I do! Everything!

HILDE: What do you mean?

73

SOLNESS: Mark my words, Hilde. Everything that I have created, beautiful, secure and friendly—yes, and magnificent too!—I must sit here and expiate. Pay for it. Not with money. But with human happiness. And not only with my happiness, but with the happiness of others, too. You see, Hilde! That's the price that my success as an artist has cost me—and others. And every day of my life I have to sit here and see that price being paid for me—day after day after day!

HILDE (*gets up and looks steadily at him*): You're thinking of *her*—aren't you?

SOLNESS: Yes. Aline had her calling in life. Just as I had mine. But she had to be destroyed and annihilated so that I could follow my calling and gain a—kind of triumph. Yes —you see, Aline had a—a talent for building, too.

HILDE: She? For building?

SOLNESS (*shakes his head*): Not houses and towers and steeples. Not the kind of things I bother with—

HILDE: Well, what, then?

SOLNESS (*softly*, *moved*): Children, Hilde. The souls of children. So that they might grow into something noble, harmonious and beautiful. So that they might become worthy human beings. That was where her talent lay. And it lies there, unused—and unusable; waste and barren, like the charred ruins left after a fire.

HILDE: Yes, but even if this were true—

SOLNESS: It is! I know it!

HILDE: Well, anyway, it's not your fault. You're not guilty.

SOLNESS: Aren't I? That's the terrible doubt that gnaws me night and day.

HILDE: This?

SOLNESS: Yes—suppose it is true. Suppose I am guilty? In a kind of way.

HILDE: You? You mean—the fire?

SOLNESS: Everything. Everything. And on the other hand— I may be quite innocent.

HILDE: Oh, master builder! If you can talk like that, you must be—well—ill, anyway.

74

SOLNESS: Hm—incurably, I'm afraid. Where this is concerned.

RAGNAR BROVIK *cautiously opens the small door in the corner on the left.* HILDE *walks across the room.*

RAGNAR (*as he sees* HILDE): Oh—I beg your pardon, Mr Solness—(*Is about to go*).

SOLNESS: No, no, come in. Let's get this matter settled.

RAGNAR: Oh, yes—if we could!

SOLNESS: Your father's no better, I hear.

RAGNAR: He's sinking fast. So—please—I beg you—write a few kind words about one of the drawings. Something he can read before he—

SOLNESS: (*violently*): You mustn't ask me any more questions about those drawings of yours.

RAGNAR: Have you looked at them?

SOLNESS: Yes—I have.

RAGNAR: And—they're no good? And I suppose I'm no good either?

SOLNESS: You stay here with me, Ragnar. You shall have whatever you want. Then you can marry Kaja, and all your cares will be over. You might even be happy. Only don't think of building by yourself.

RAGNAR: Very well. I'd better go home and tell father that. I promised him I would. Shall I tell father this—before he dies?

SOLNESS (*distressed*): Oh, tell him—tell him what you like. Better not tell him anything. (*Violently*) I can't help it, Ragnar. I have no choice.

RAGNAR: In that case, may I have the drawings?

SOLNESS: Yes, take them—take them away. They're on the table.

RAGNAR (*goes across*): Thank you.

HILDE (*puts her hand on the portfolio*): No, no, leave them.

SOLNESS: Why?

HILDE: I'd like to look at them, too.

SOLNESS: But you've already—(*To* RAGNAR) All right, then. Leave them there.

75

RAGNAR: By all means.

SOLNESS: And now go home to your father.

RAGNAR: I suppose I must.

SOLNESS (*as though desperate*): Ragnar—you mustn't ask of me something I cannot do! Do you hear, Ragnar? You mustn't do that!

RAGNAR: No, no. I'm sorry. (*Bows and goes out through the corner door.* HILDE *goes and sits on a chair by the mirror*).

HILDE (*looks angrily at* SOLNESS): That was beastly of you.

SOLNESS: You think so, too?

HILDE: Yes, really beastly. Hard and vicious and cruel.

SOLNESS: Oh, you don't understand.

HILDE: All the same—no, you shouldn't be like that. Not you.

SOLNESS: You said yourself just now that I was the only person who should be allowed to build.

HILDE: I can say that. Not you.

SOLNESS: If anyone can, I can. I paid dearly enough for my position.

HILDE: Oh, yes. Domestic bliss, and all that.

SOLNESS: Peace of mind.

HILDE (*gets up*): Peace of mind! (*With feeling*) Yes, of course! Poor master builder! You fancy that—

SOLNESS (*chuckles*): You sit down again, Hilde, and I'll tell you a funny story.

HILDE (*sits*): Well?

SOLNESS: It sounds so ludicrously trivial. You see, it all turns on a crack in a chimney pipe.

HILDE: That all?

SOLNESS: Yes, to begin with. (*He moves a chair closer to* HILDE, *and sits*).

HILDE (*impatient, slaps her knee*): So there was a crack in the chimney?

SOLNESS: I'd noticed that crack for a long time, long before the fire. Each time I went up to the loft, I looked to see if it was still there.

HILDE: And it was?

SOLNESS: Yes. No one else knew about it.

76

HILDE: And you didn't say anything?

SOLNESS: No, I didn't.

HILDE: And you didn't think of getting it mended?

SOLNESS: Oh, I thought about it, but I didn't do anything.
Each time I decided to get down to it, it was just as though
a hand reached out and held me back. Not today, I thought.
Tomorrow. So nothing ever came of it.

HILDE: Why did you always put it off?

SOLNESS: Because a thought had occurred to me. (*Slow,
quiet*) "Through this little black crack in this chimney
pipe, I might climb my way to the top. Become a master
builder."

HILDE (*to herself*): That must have been exciting.

SOLNESS: It was irresistible—almost. Utterly irresistible!
At the time, it all seemed so unimportant and trivial. I
wanted it to happen some time in winter. Shortly before
dinner. I would be out, driving Aline in the sleigh.
The servants would have built up great fires in all the
rooms—

HILDE: It'd be frightfully cold that day, wouldn't it?

SOLNESS: Pretty sharp, yes. And they'd want it to be good and
warm for Aline when she came back.

HILDE: Yes, she suffers from the cold, doesn't she?

SOLNESS: She does. And then, it'd be on the way home that
we'd see the smoke.

HILDE: Just the smoke?

SOLNESS: First of all the smoke. But then, when we reached
the drive, the old crate was just a surging mass of flames!
That's the way I wanted it to happen.

HILDE: Oh, why couldn't it have happened like that?
(*Pause*) But, wait a moment, master builder. Are you quite
sure that the fire was caused by this little crack in the
chimney?

SOLNESS: No, on the contrary. I'm quite sure the crack in the
chimney had nothing whatever to do with the fire.

HILDE: What!

SOLNESS: It's been established that the fire broke out in the
linen room, on the other side of the house.

HILDE: Then why on earth are you sitting here drivelling about this cracked chimney?

SOLNESS: May I go on talking to you for a little, Hilde?

HILDE: Yes, but only if you talk sensibly.

SOLNESS: I'll do my best. (*Moves his chair closer*).

HILDE: Well! Out with it, master builder!

SOLNESS (*confidentially*): Don't you think, Hilde, that there are people singled out by fate who have been endowed with grace and power to wish for something, desire it so passionately, *will* it so inexorably that, ultimately, they must be granted it? Don't you think so?

HILDE (*with an enigmatic expression in her eyes*): If that is so, the time will come when we shall see if I am one of them.

SOLNESS: No man can achieve such things alone. Oh, no. There are—helpers and servants—who must be at our side if we are to succeed. But they never come of their own accord. One must call on them with all one's strength. Silently, you understand.

HILDE: Who are these helpers and servants?

SOLNESS: Oh, let's talk about that some other time. For the moment, let's concentrate on the fire.

HILDE: Don't you think there would have been a fire even if you hadn't wished for it?

SOLNESS: If that house had been owned by old Knut Brovik, it would never have burned down at such an opportune moment. I'm sure of that. Because he doesn't understand how to call on the helpers, or to summon those who serve him. (*Gets up restlessly*) So you see, Hilde—it *is* I who am guilty, and both those little boys had to pay with their lives. And is it not also true that it is my fault that Aline has not become what she should and could have become? And what she so longed to become.

HILDE: Yes, but if it's these helpers and servants who—

SOLNESS: Who called to the helpers and to the servants? I did! And they came and bowed to my will. (*In increasing turmoil*) This is what people call being lucky. But I'll tell you how it feels to be lucky! It feels as though the skin had been flayed from my breast. And the helpers and servants

78

go round taking the skin from other people's bodies to cover the wound. But it can't be healed. Never, never! Oh, if you only knew how it burns sometimes.

HILDE: You are ill, master builder. Very ill, I think.

SOLNESS: Say mad. That's what you mean.

HILDE: No, I don't think there's anything wrong with your head.

SOLNESS: What, then? Out with it!

HILDE: I'm wondering if you weren't born with an under-developed conscience.

SOLNESS: Under-developed conscience? What the devil do you mean?

HILDE: I mean that your conscience is very frail. Over-sensitive; won't get to grips with things. Can't carry a heavy burden.

SOLNESS (*growls*): Hm! How ought a conscience to be, if I may ask?

HILDE: In your case I wish it were a little more—well—robust.

SOLNESS: Indeed? Robust? Well! And have you a robust conscience?

HILDE: Yes, I think so. I haven't noticed anything to the contrary.

SOLNESS: I don't suppose you've had much opportunity to test it, have you?

HILDE (*with a tremble round her mouth*): Oh, it wasn't all that easy to leave father. I'm frightfully fond of him.

SOLNESS: Oh, just for a month or two—

HILDE: I don't think I shall ever go back.

SOLNESS: What, never? Why did you leave him, then?

HILDE (*half serious, half teasing*): Have you forgotten again? The ten years are up!

SOLNESS: Nonsense. Was there anything wrong at home? Mm?

HILDE (*earnestly*): This thing inside me drove me to come here. Tempted and drove me.

SOLNESS (*eagerly*): That's it! That's it, Hilde! There's troll in you, too; the same as in me. And it's the troll, you see,

79

that calls to the powers outside! And we have to submit whether we like it or not.

HILDE: I begin to think you're right, master builder.

SOLNESS (*paces the floor*): Oh, there are so many invisible demons in the world, Hilde. (*Stops*) Good demons and evil demons. Fair demons and dark. If only one always knew whether it was the fair that had hold of one, or the dark! (*Starts walking again*) Ha, ha! It would all be so simple.

HILDE (*watches him as he walks*): Or if only one had a really brash and hearty conscience! So that one dared to do what one wanted.

SOLNESS (*stops by the console table*): Oh, I think most people are as cowardly as I, in that respect.

HILDE: That may well be.

SOLNESS (*leans against the table*): In the sagas—have you read any of those old sagas?

HILDE: Oh, yes! In the days when I used to read—

SOLNESS: Those sagas tell about vikings, who sailed to foreign lands and plundered and burned and killed—

HILDE: And carried away women—

SOLNESS: And kept them—

HILDE: Took them home with them in their ships—

SOLNESS: And used them like—like the worst kind of trolls.

HILDE (*to herself, with her eyes half closed*): I think that must be so exciting!

SOLNESS (*with a short, gruff laugh*): To take a woman, you mean?

HILDE: To be taken.

SOLNESS (*looks at her for a moment*): I see.

HILDE (*as though changing the subject*): But what were you going to say about these vikings, master builder?

SOLNESS: Oh, yes—well, those fellows, their consciences were robust enough. When they came home, they ate and drank, and were as merry as children. And what about the women! Quite often they didn't want to leave these men! Can you understand that, Hilde?

HILDE: I can understand the women frightfully well.

SOLNESS: Ah! Perhaps you would do the same yourself?

HILDE: Why not?

SOLNESS: Live—willingly—with a brute like that?

HILDE: If he was a brute I'd come to grow really fond of—

SOLNESS: *Could* you grow fond of a man like that?

HILDE: Oh, God, one can't help whom one grows fond of, can one?

SOLNESS (*looks at her thoughtfully*): No, no—I suppose it's the troll in us that decides that.

HILDE (*with a little laugh*): And all these blessed demons you know so much about. The fair and the dark.

SOLNESS (*warmly and quietly*): I hope the demons choose kindly for you, Hilde.

HILDE: They have chosen for me. Once and for all.

SOLNESS (*looks deep into her eyes*): Hilde—you are like a wild bird of the forest.

HILDE: Far from it. I'm not shy.

SOLNESS: No, no. There's more of the falcon in you.

HILDE: Yes—perhaps. (*Violently*) And why not a falcon? Why shouldn't I go hunting, too? Get the prey I want? If only I can get my claws into it! Bring it to the ground!

SOLNESS: Hilde—do you know what you are?

HILDE: Yes, I'm a strange kind of bird.

SOLNESS: No. You are like a new dawn. When I look at you, it is as though I were watching the sunrise.

HILDE: Tell me, master builder—are you sure you've never called to me? Silently?

SOLNESS (*quietly*): I think I must have done.

HILDE: What do you want from me?

SOLNESS: Your youth, Hilde.

HILDE (*smiles*): Youth, which you are so frightened of?

SOLNESS (*nods slowly*): And which, in my heart, I long for.

HILDE *gets up, goes over to the small table, and fetches* RAGNAR BROVIK'S *portfolio*.

HILDE (*holds out the portfolio towards him*): What about these drawings, now?

SOLNESS (*curtly*): Put those things away. I've seen enough of them.

HILDE: Quite, but you're going to approve them.

SOLNESS: Approve them? I'm damned if I will.

HILDE: Can't you do this little thing for him? The poor old man's dying. And then perhaps his son might get the chance to build the house, too.

SOLNESS: Yes, that's just it. He can. He's made sure of that, that young gentleman.

HILDE: Well, for goodness sake, if he has, can't you bring yourself to lie a tiny little bit?

SOLNESS: Lie? (*Furiously*) Hilde, take those damned drawings away from me!

HILDE (*draws the portfolio a little towards her*): Now, now, now, don't snap at me. You talk about trolls. I think you behave like one yourself. (*Looks round*) Where do you keep your pen and ink?

SOLNESS: I haven't any in here.

HILDE (*goes towards the door*): Well, that girl'll have some—

SOLNESS: Stay where you are, Hilde! I must tell a lie, you said. Oh, I wouldn't mind doing it for his old father. A man I once ruined.

HILDE: You ruined him too?

SOLNESS: I needed room. But this young Ragnar—he mustn't on any account be allowed to come to the front.

HILDE: He won't, either, will he, poor boy? If he's no good—

SOLNESS (*comes closer, looks at her and whispers*): If Ragnar Brovik gets started, he will break me. Just as I broke his father.

HILDE: Break *you*? He is some good, then?

SOLNESS: Yes, he's good, make no mistake. He is the youth who is waiting ready to bang upon my door. And make an end of master builder Solness.

HILDE: And yet you wanted to shut him out? For shame, master builder!

SOLNESS: This struggle has cost me enough. Besides, I'm afraid the helpers and the servants won't obey me any longer.

HILDE: Then you'll have to manage on your own. There's nothing for it.

SOLNESS: Hopeless, Hilde. The tide will turn. Sooner or later. Retribution will come.

HILDE (*frightened, puts her hands over her ears*): Don't talk like that! Do you want to take away from me what I value more than my life?

SOLNESS: And what's that?

HILDE: To see you great! See you with a wreath in your hand! High, high up on a church tower! (*Calm again*) Well, at least you must have a pencil. Give it to me.

SOLNESS (*takes out his notebook*): Yes, I've got one here.

HILDE (*puts the portfolio on the table by the sofa*): Right. And now we'll sit down here, master builder.

SOLNESS *sits at the table.*

HILDE (*behind him, leaning over the back of his chair*): And then we'll write on the drawings. Really, really nicely and kindly, we'll write. For this beastly Ragnvald or whatever his name is.

SOLNESS (*writes a few lines, turns and looks up at her*): Tell me something, Hilde.

HILDE: Yes?

SOLNESS: If you've really been waiting for me for ten years—

HILDE: Well?

SOLNESS: Why didn't you write to me?

HILDE (*quickly*): No, no, no! That was just what I didn't want!

SOLNESS: Why not?

HILDE: I was afraid that then it might all go wrong. But we were going to write on the drawings, master builder.

SOLNESS: So we were.

HILDE (*leans over him and watches while he writes*): How good and kind. Oh, how I hate—how I hate this Ragnvald—

SOLNESS (*as he writes*): Have you never been—really fond of anyone, Hilde?

HILDE (*in a hard voice*): What did you say?

SOLNESS: I asked if you had ever been really fond of anyone.

HILDE: Anyone else, you mean?

SOLNESS (*looks up at her*): Yes, of course—anyone else. Haven't you? In all these years? Ever?

HILDE: Oh, yes, once in a while. When I was really mad with you for not coming.

SOLNESS: Then you—cared about others too?

HILDE: A little. For a week or two. Oh, God, master builder, you know how it is.

SOLNESS: Hilde—why have you come?

HILDE: Don't waste time. That poor old man may be dying while you talk.

SOLNESS: Answer me, Hilde. What is it you want from me?

HILDE: I want my kingdom.

SOLNESS: Hm—

He glances quickly towards the door on the left, and continues writing on the drawings. MRS SOLNESS enters, carrying some parcels.

MRS SOLNESS: I've brought you a few things, Miss Wangel. There are some big parcels being sent on later.

HILDE: Oh, how very sweet of you!

MRS SOLNESS: It's my simple duty. That's all.

SOLNESS (*reading through what he has written*): Aline!

MRS SOLNESS: Yes?

SOLNESS: Did you see if she—if the book-keeper was out there?

MRS SOLNESS: Yes, of course she was there.

SOLNESS (*replacing the drawings in the portfolio*): Hm—

MRS SOLNESS: She was standing at the desk, as she always does—when I'm in the room.

SOLNESS (*gets up*): I'll give this to her, then, and tell her that—

HILDE (*taking the portfolio from him*): Oh, no, let me, please! (*Goes to the door, then turns*) What's her name?

SOLNESS: Her name's Miss Fosli.

HILDE: Ugh, that sounds so formal. What's her first name, I mean?

SOLNESS: Kaja, I think.

HILDE (*opens the door and calls*): Kaja! Come in here. Hurry! The master builder wants to speak to you.

KAJA *comes inside the door.*

KAJA (*looks at him, frightened*): Here I am—?

HILDE (*holds out the portfolio to her*): Look, Kaja! You can take this, now. The master builder's written on them.

KAJA: Oh—at last!

SOLNESS: Give them to the old man as soon as you can.

KAJA: I'll take them home at once.

SOLNESS: Yes, do that. And then Ragnar can begin to build.

KAJA: Oh, may he come and thank you for everything—?

SOLNESS: I want no thanks. Tell him so from me.

KAJA: Yes, I'll—

SOLNESS: And tell him at the same time that from now on I've no use for him. Nor for you.

KAJA (*quietly trembling*): Nor for me?

SOLNESS: You'll have other things to think about now. And someone else to look after. And that's as it should be. All right, go home now with your drawings, Miss Fosli. Quickly! Do you hear?

KAJA: Yes, Mr Solness. (*Goes out*).

MRS SOLNESS: Oh, what sly eyes she has!

SOLNESS: That poor little creature?

MRS SOLNESS: Oh, I'm not blind, Halvard. Are you really dismissing them?

SOLNESS: Yes.

MRS SOLNESS: Her too?

SOLNESS: Well, wasn't that what you wanted?

MRS SOLNESS: But how can you manage without her? Oh, I see; you've someone else up your sleeve, haven't you, Halvard?

HILDE (*gaily*): Well, I'm no good for standing at desks, anyway.

SOLNESS: I shall manage somehow, Aline. You must make arrangements for moving into our new home as soon as possible. This evening we shall hoist the wreath—(*Turns*

85

to HILDE)—to the top of the spire. What do you say to that, Miss Hilde?

HILDE (*looks at him excitedly*): It'll be so marvellous to see you standing high up there again!

SOLNESS: Me!

MRS SOLNESS: Oh God, Miss Wangel, you mustn't think of it! My husband gets dizzy. He has no head for heights.

HILDE: Dizzy? I don't believe it.

MRS SOLNESS: Oh, yes, he's always been like that.

HILDE: But I've seen him myself high up on the top of a church steeple.

MRS SOLNESS: Yes, I've heard people talk about that. But it's impossible.

SOLNESS (*violently*): Impossible, yes! But nevertheless, I stood up there!

MRS SOLNESS: How can you say that, Halvard? You hardly even dare to go out on to the balcony on the second floor. You've always been like that.

SOLNESS: You may think otherwise this evening.

MRS SOLNESS (*frightened*): No, no, no! God will help me to prevent that! I'll write a message to the doctor at once. He'll talk you out of it.

SOLNESS: But Aline—

MRS SOLNESS: Yes, you're ill, Halvard! That's what it is, you're ill! Oh God, oh God—! (*She hurries out to the right*).

HILDE (*looks at him tensely*): Is it true?

SOLNESS: That I have no head for heights?

HILDE: That *my* master builder dare not—cannot—rise as high as he can build?

SOLNESS: That is how you see it?

HILDE: Yes.

SOLNESS: I begin to think there is nothing in me that is safe from you.

HILDE (*looks towards the bay window*): Up there! Right up there!

SOLNESS (*goes closer*): You could live up there, Hilde. In the highest room in the tower. You could live there like a princess.

HILDE (*enigmatically, half-serious, half-jesting*): Yes, that's what you promised me.

SOLNESS: Did I?

HILDE: For shame, master builder! You said you'd make me a princess, and that you would give me a kingdom. And then you took me and— Well?

SOLNESS (*gently*): Are you quite sure it wasn't a dream? Something you just imagined?

HILDE (*sharply*): You think you didn't do it?

SOLNESS: I hardly know myself—(*More quietly*) But I know one thing—that I—

HILDE: That you—? Say it!

SOLNESS: That I should have done it.

HILDE (*suddenly gay*): *You*—dizzy!

SOLNESS: Tonight we shall hang up our wreath, Princess Hilde.

HILDE (*with a touch of bitterness*): Over your new home.

SOLNESS: Over the new house. It will never be a home for me. (*He goes out through the garden door*).

HILDE (*with half closed eyes, whispers to herself. Only two words can be heard*) . . . frightfully exciting . . .

ACT THREE

A large, broad verandah belonging to Solness's house. Part of the house, with a door leading to the verandah, can be seen on the left. In front, to the right, a railing. Backstage, at one end of the verandah, a flight of steps leads down to the garden below. Large old trees stretch their branches over the verandah towards the house. On the extreme right, through the trees, can be glimpsed the lower part of the new villa, with scaffolding round the base of the tower. Backstage, the garden is bounded by an old fence. Beyond the fence is a street, with low, tumbledown cottages. Evening sky, with clouds irradiated by the sun.

On the verandah, against the wall of the house, stands a garden seat, and in front of the seat is a long table. On the other side of the table, an armchair and some stools. All the furniture is of wicker.

MRS SOLNESS, wrapped in a large, white crepe shawl, is resting in the armchair, gazing over towards the right. After a few moments, HILDE WANGEL comes up the steps from the garden. She is dressed as before, and is wearing her hat. On her breast is pinned a little bouquet of common flowers.

MRS SOLNESS (*turns her head slightly*): Have you been in the garden, Miss Wangel?

HILDE: Yes, I've been having a look round.

MRS SOLNESS: You've found some flowers too, I see.

HILDE: Oh, yes. There are heaps of them. Among the bushes.

MRS SOLNESS: No, are there really? Still? I hardly ever go down there.

HILDE (*comes closer*): What? I should have thought you'd skip down every day.

MRS SOLNESS (*smiles wanly*): I don't skip anywhere, I'm afraid. Not any longer.

HILDE: But don't you go down now and then to say hullo to all the beautiful things there?

MRS SOLNESS: It's all become so foreign to me. I'm almost afraid to look at it again.

HILDE: Your own garden?

MRS SOLNESS: I don't feel it's mine any longer.

HILDE: Oh, what rubbish!

MRS SOLNESS: No, no, it isn't. It's not like it was in mother's and father's time. They've taken such a dreadful lot of it away, Miss Wangel. Can you imagine? They've broken it up, and built houses in it, for strangers! People I don't know. They can look at me from their windows.

HILDE (*with a sunny expression*): Mrs. Solness?

MRS SOLNESS: Yes?

HILDE: May I sit here with you for a little?

MRS SOLNESS: Yes, please do, if you'd really like to.

HILDE *moves a stool close to the armchair and sits on it.*

HILDE: Ah, one can sit and sun oneself here. Like a cat.

MRS SOLNESS (*puts her hand gently on* HILDE'S *neck*): It's very sweet of you to want to sit with me. I thought you were going inside to my husband.

HILDE: What would I want with him?

MRS SOLNESS: I thought you'd want to help him.

HILDE: No, thank you. Anyway, he's not in. He's over there among the workmen. But he looked so fierce I didn't dare to talk to him.

MRS SOLNESS: Oh, he's very soft and gentle really.

HILDE: *He?*

MRS SOLNESS: You don't know him well enough yet, Miss Wangel.

HILDE (*looks affectionately at her*): Are you happy to be moving over to the new house?

MRS SOLNESS: I should be happy. That's what Halvard wants.

HILDE: Oh, I didn't mean just because of that.

MRS SOLNESS: Yes, Miss Wangel, yes. That's my duty, don't

you see, to do what he wants. But it's often so difficult to force oneself to be obedient.

HILDE: Yes, that must be difficult.

MRS SOLNESS: Yes, indeed. When one's as weak a person as I am—

HILDE: When one has suffered as much as you have—

MRS SOLNESS: How do you know that?

HILDE: Your husband told me.

MRS SOLNESS: He so seldom speaks to me about these things. Yes, I've had more than my share of suffering in my lifetime, Miss Wangel.

HILDE (*looks at her sympathetically, and nods slowly*): Poor Mrs Solness. First there was the fire—

MRS SOLNESS (*sighs*): Yes. Everything I had was burned.

HILDE: And then there was worse to follow.

MRS SOLNESS: Worse?

HILDE: The worst thing of all.

MRS SOLNESS: What do you mean?

HILDE (*quietly*): You lost both your little boys.

MRS SOLNESS: Oh, them, yes. Well, that was different. That was an Act of God. One must resign oneself to such things. And be thankful.

HILDE: Are you?

MRS SOLNESS: Not always, I'm afraid. I know so well that it's my duty. But I can't.

HILDE: No, well, I think that's very understandable.

MRS SOLNESS: Time and again I have to remind myself that I've been justly punished—

HILDE: Why?

MRS SOLNESS: Because I wasn't resolute enough in the face of adversity.

HILDE: But I don't see that—

MRS SOLNESS: No, no, Miss Wangel—don't talk to me any more about the two little boys. We should be happy for them. They're so much, much better off where they are. No, it's the little losses which leave the deepest wound. Things which other people would regard as unimportant.

HILDE (*puts her arms on MRS SOLNESS'S knee and looks up at her warmly*): Dear Mrs Solness, tell me—what kind of things?

MRS SOLNESS: Just little things. All the old portraits on the walls were burned. And all the old silk dresses, that had been in our family for generations. And all mama's and grandmama's lace, that was burned too. And think of the jewels! (*Sadly*) And—all the dolls.

HILDE: The dolls?

MRS SOLNESS (*tearfully*): I had nine beautiful dolls.

HILDE: And they were burned too?

MRS SOLNESS: All of them. Oh, it was so hard for me—so hard.

HILDE: Had you kept all those dolls, then? Ever since you'd been a child?

MRS SOLNESS: I didn't just keep them. They lived with me.

HILDE: After you'd grown up?

MRS SOLNESS: Yes, long after.

HILDE: After you were married?

MRS SOLNESS: Oh, yes. As long as he didn't see them— But then they were burned, poor dears. No one thought of saving them. Oh, it makes me so sad to think about it. Now you mustn't laugh at me, Miss Wangel.

HILDE: I'm not laughing.

MRS SOLNESS: They were alive, too, in a way, you see. I carried them under my heart. Like little unborn children.

DR HERDAL, *hat in hand, comes out through the door and catches sight of* MRS SOLNESS *and* HILDE.

HERDAL: Giving yourself a cold, I see, Mrs Solness!

MRS SOLNESS: I think it's so nice and warm out here today.

HERDAL: Yes, yes. But is something the matter? I got a note—

MRS SOLNESS (*gets up*): Yes, there's something I have to talk to you about.

HERDAL: By all means. Perhaps we'd better go inside. (*To* HILDE) Still wearing your climbing outfit, young lady?

HILDE (*gaily, as she gets up*): Rather! Dressed to kill! No climbing for me today, though. You and I will stay down here and watch like good little children.

HERDAL: Watch what?

MRS SOLNESS (*quietly, frightened, to* HILDE): Ssh, please, for heaven's sake! He's coming! Try to dissuade him from this idea! And—do let us be friends, Miss Wangel. Can't we?

HILDE (*throws her arms impetuously round* MRS SOLNESS'S *neck*): Oh, if only we could!

MRS SOLNESS (*frees herself, gently*): Now, now, now. Here he comes, Doctor. Let me talk to you for a moment.

HERDAL: Is it about him?

MRS SOLNESS: Yes, it's about him. Come inside.

She and the DOCTOR *go into the house. The next moment,* SOLNESS *comes up the steps from the garden. A serious expression comes over* HILDE'S *face.*

SOLNESS (*glances at the door as it is carefully shut from inside*): Have you noticed, Hilde? As soon as I come, she goes.

HILDE: I've noticed that when you come that makes her go.

SOLNESS: Possibly. But I can't help that. (*Looks closely at her*) Are you cold, Hilde? You look as if you were.

HILDE: I've just come up out of a tomb.

SOLNESS: What does that mean?

HILDE: The frost's got into me, master builder.

SOLNESS (*slowly*): I think I understand—

HILDE: Why have you come up here?

SOLNESS: I saw you.

HILDE: You must have seen her, too.

SOLNESS: I knew she'd go as soon as I came.

HILDE: Does it hurt you that she always avoids you?

SOLNESS: In a way it's a kind of relief.

HILDE: That you don't always have to be looking at her?

SOLNESS: Yes.

HILDE: That you don't have to be reminded the whole time of how much she grieves for her little boys?

SOLNESS: Yes. That above all.

HILDE wanders along the verandah with her hands behind her back, stops by the railing and gazes out across the garden.

SOLNESS: How long did you talk to her?

HILDE *does not move or reply.*

SOLNESS: How long, I asked?

HILDE *remains silent.*

SOLNESS: What did she talk about, then?

HILDE *still does not speak.*

SOLNESS: Poor Aline! About the children, I suppose.

HILDE *shivers nervously, then nods twice rapidly.*

SOLNESS: She can't get over it. She will never get over it. (*Goes closer*) Now you're standing there like a statue again. You stood like that last night.

HILDE (*turns and looks at him, large-eyed, serious*): I want to go.

SOLNESS (*sharply*): Go?

HILDE: Yes.

SOLNESS: No. I won't allow it.

HILDE: What can I do here now?

SOLNESS: Just—stay here, Hilde.

HILDE (*looks at him scornfully*): Thank you very much. But it wouldn't end there.

SOLNESS (*impulsively*): So much the better!

HILDE (*violently*): I can't hurt someone I *know*. I can't take what belongs to her.

SOLNESS: Who says you will?

HILDE: From a stranger, yes. That's different. Someone I've never set eyes on. But someone I've got close to—! No! No! Ugh!

SOLNESS: But I haven't suggested that you should.

HILDE: Oh, master builder, you know very well how it would end. That's why I'm leaving.

SOLNESS: And what's to become of me when you've gone? What shall I have to live for? Afterwards?

HILDE (*with the enigmatic expression in her eyes*): It's easy for you. You have your duty to her. You must live for that duty.

SOLNESS: Too late. These powers—these—

HILDE: Demons—

SOLNESS: Yes, demons. And the troll in me. They've sucked her blood. (*Laughs desperately*) It was done for my happiness. (*Heavily*) And for my sake she died. And I am chained to the corpse. (*In anguish*) I—I, who cannot live without joy!

HILDE *walks round the table and sits down on the seat with her elbows on the table, leaning her head on her hands.*

HILDE (*sits of a moment, looking at him*): What are you going to build next?

SOLNESS (*shakes his head*): I don't think I shall build much more.

HILDE: No more happy homes for mummy and daddy? And all the little children?

SOLNESS: God knows whether people will want that kind of thing any more.

HILDE: Poor master builder! And you've spent ten years thinking of nothing else? You've given your life to it.

SOLNESS: I have, haven't I, Hilde?

HILDE (*bursts out*): Oh, I think it's all so wrong, so wrong!

SOLNESS: What?

HILDE: That one should be afraid to seize happiness! To seize hold of life! Just because someone stands in the way. Someone one knows.

SOLNESS: Someone one has no right to pass by.

HILDE: Haven't we that right, I wonder? But even so— Oh, if one could only sleep and forget it all! (*She lays her arms flat on the table, rests her left cheek on her hands and closes her eyes*).

SOLNESS (*turns the armchair round and sits down by the table*): Did you have a happy home with your father, Hilde?

HILDE (*without moving, replies as though half asleep*): I only had a cage.

SOLNESS: And you don't want to go back into it?

HILDE (*as before*): Wild birds don't fly into cages.

SOLNESS: They want to chase the free air—

HILDE (*still in the same tone*): Eagles love the chase.

SOLNESS (*resting his eyes on her*): If only one were a viking. They had hunting in their blood.

HILDE (*opens her eyes, but does not move, and says in her normal voice*): What else did they have? Tell me!

SOLNESS: A robust conscience.

HILDE *sits up, alive. Her eyes are again excited and aflame.*

HILDE (*nodding*): I know what you're going to build next!

SOLNESS: Then you know more than I do, Hilde.

HILDE: Yes. Master builders are very stupid people.

SOLNESS: What is it to be, then?

HILDE (*nods again*): The castle.

SOLNESS: What castle?

HILDE: *My* castle, of course.

SOLNESS: You want a castle, now?

HILDE: You owe me a kingdom, don't you?

SOLNESS: So you tell me.

HILDE: Well, then! You owe me this kingdom. And a kingdom's got to have a castle, hasn't it?

SOLNESS (*more and more exhilarated*): Yes, they usually do.

HILDE: Good. Build it for me then! At once!

SOLNESS (*laughs*): Within the hour?

HILDE: Yes! The ten years are up now. And I don't intend to wait any longer. I want my castle, master builder!

SOLNESS: It's no joke to have you as a creditor, Hilde.

HILDE: You should have thought of that before. Now it's too late. Now then! (*Thumps on the table*) Where's my castle? It's *my* castle!

SOLNESS (*more earnestly, leans closer to her, with his arms on the table*): What does it look like, this castle of yours, Hilde?

HILDE (*slowly*): My castle must stand high up. High above everything. Open and free on every side. So that I can see for miles around.

SOLNESS: It's got a tower, I suppose?

HILDE: A frightfully high tower. And right up on the top of the tower there'll be a balcony. And that's where I shall stand—

SOLNESS (*involuntarily clutches his head*): How can you want to stand so high? Doesn't it make you giddy—?

95

HILDE: I want to stand up there and look down at the others —the ones who build churches. And homes for mothers and fathers and children. And you can come up there and look down too.

SOLNESS (*humbly*): Has the master builder leave to climb up to the princess?

HILDE: If the master builder wishes.

SOLNESS (*whispers*): Then—I think the master builder will come.

HILDE (*nods*): The master builder—he will come.

SOLNESS: But he will never build again. Poor master builder!

HILDE (*alive*): Oh, yes he will! We'll do it together! And we'll build the most beautiful thing—the most beautiful thing in the world!

SOLNESS: Hilde—tell me. What is that?

HILDE (*looks at him with a smile, give a little shake of her head, pouts and says, as though to a child*): Master builders—they are vewy—vewy stupid people.

SOLNESS: Yes, they're stupid, I know. But tell me—what is the most beautiful thing in the world? The thing we two are going to build together?

HILDE (*is silent for a moment, then says, with the enigmatic expression in her eyes*): A castle in the air.

SOLNESS: A castle in the air?

HILDE (*nods*): A castle in the air, yes. Do you know what a castle in the air is?

SOLNESS: It's the most beautiful thing in the world, you say.

HILDE (*jumps up angrily and makes a contemptuous gesture with her hand*): Yes, of course! Castles in the air are so safe to hide in. And easy to build. (*Looks at him scornfully*) Especially for master builders with a—a giddy conscience.

SOLNESS (*gets up*): From now on we two shall build together, Hilde.

HILDE (*with a doubting smile*): A real castle in the air?

SOLNESS: Yes. Built on a true foundation.

RAGNAR BROVIK *comes out of the house. He is carrying a big, green wreath with flowers and silk ribbons.*

HILDE (*exclaims joyfully*): The wreath! Oh, it's going to be absolutely marvellous!

SOLNESS (*amazed*): Have you brought the wreath, Ragnar?

RAGNAR: I promised the foreman I would.

SOLNESS (*relieved*): Your father's better, then?

RAGNAR: No.

SOLNESS: Didn't it cheer him up, what I wrote?

RAGNAR: It came too late.

SOLNESS: Too late!

RAGNAR: By the time she came with it, he'd lost consciousness. He'd had a stroke.

SOLNESS: Get back home to him, then. Look after your father.

RAGNAR: He doesn't need me any more.

SOLNESS: But surely you ought to be with him?

RAGNAR: She's sitting with him.

SOLNESS (*a little uncertainly*): Kaja?

RAGNAR (*looks darkly at him*): Yes. Kaja.

SOLNESS: Go home, Ragnar. Go home to them. Give me the wreath.

RAGNAR (*represses a scornful smile*): Surely *you're* not going to—?

SOLNESS: I'll take it down there myself. (*Takes the wreath from him*) Go home, now. We won't need you today.

RAGNAR: I know you won't. But today, I'm staying.

SOLNESS: Oh, stay—stay, by all means.

HILDE (*at the railing*): Master builder—I shall stand here and watch you.

SOLNESS: Watch me?

HILDE: It'll be frightfully exciting.

SOLNESS (*subdued*): We'll—talk about that later, Hilde. (*He descends the steps with the wreath and goes out through the garden*).

HILDE (*watches him go, then turns to* RAGNAR): You might at least have thanked him.

RAGNAR: Thanked him? Should I have thanked *him*?

HILDE: Yes, you should.

RAGNAR: I ought to thank you, if anyone.

HILDE: How can you say such a thing?

RAGNAR: But you watch out. You don't know him yet.

HILDE (*angrily*): I know him better than anyone.

RAGNAR (*laughs bitterly*): Thank *him*, who's kept me back year after year? Who made my father lose his belief in me? Made me lose belief in myself. And all just so that he could—

HILDE (*as though sensing his meaning*): So that he could—what? Tell me.

RAGNAR: So that he could keep *her*.

HILDE (*with a movement towards him*): The girl at the desk?

RAGNAR: Yes.

HILDE (*clenches her fists*): It's not true! You're lying!

RAGNAR: I didn't want to believe it either, until today. When she told me.

HILDE: What did she tell you? I want to know! Now! Now!

RAGNAR: She said he'd taken possession of her mind. That he'd directed all her thoughts towards himself. She says she'll never be able to free herself from him. That she'll stay wherever he is—

HILDE: She won't!

RAGNAR: Who's going to stop her? Are you?

HILDE (*quickly*): I won't be the only one.

RAGNAR: Oh yes. I see. Now she'd only be a nuisance to him.

HILDE: You don't understand anything, if you talk like that. No, I'll tell you why he kept her on.

RAGNAR: Why?

HILDE: To keep you.

RAGNAR: Did he tell you that?

HILDE: No, but it's true! It *must* be! (*Wildly*) It is, it is, I want it to be!

RAGNAR: And the moment *you* came, he let her go.

HILDE: It was *you* he let go! What do you think he cares about girls like her?

RAGNAR (*thoughtfully*): You mean he's been afraid of me all these years?

HILDE: Afraid of you? You fancy yourself!

RAGNAR: Oh, he must have realized a long time ago that I've got something in me. Besides—afraid—that's just what he is, don't you see?

HILDE: Try to make me believe that!

RAGNAR: In some ways he's afraid. The great master builder! Oh, he's not afraid to destroy people's happiness, the way he has father's and mine. But ask him to climb up a few feet of scaffolding, and he'll go down on his knees and pray to God to be delivered.

HILDE: Oh, if only you'd seen him high up there! As giddily high as I once saw him!

RAGNAR: Have you seen that?

HILDE: Yes, I've seen it. Oh, so proud and free he stood up there as he tied the wreath to the church weathercock!

RAGNAR: I know he dared to do it once in his life. Just once. We've often talked about it. But no power on earth will persuade him to do it again.

HILDE: He'll do it today.

RAGNAR: Don't you believe it.

HILDE: You'll see.

RAGNAR: I won't, and neither will you.

HILDE (*violently, uncontrollably*): I will! I will—I *must* see it!

RAGNAR: But he won't do it. He just daren't. He's got this yellow streak—the great master builder!

MRS SOLNESS *comes out of the house on to the verandah.*

MRS SOLNESS (*looking round*): Isn't he here? Where's he gone?

RAGNAR: The master builder is over there with the workmen.

HILDE: He took the wreath.

MRS SOLNESS (*in terror*): Took the wreath? Oh, my God, my God! Brovik—you must go down to him! Get him to come back here!

RAGNAR: Shall I say you want to speak to him?

MRS SOLNESS: Oh, yes, my dear boy, please do. No, no—don't tell him I want him. Tell him there's someone here. That he must come at once.

RAGNAR: Very well. I'll tell him that, Mrs Solness. (*He goes down the steps and out through the garden*).

99

MRS SOLNESS: Oh, Miss Wangel, you can't imagine how frightened I am for him.

HILDE: But what is there to be so frightened about?

MRS SOLNESS: Suppose he's serious! Suppose he takes it into his head to climb up the scaffolding!

HILDE (*tensely*): Do you think he will?

MRS SOLNESS: Oh, one can never be sure what he might do. He's quite capable of doing anything.

HILDE: Oh, so you, too, think he's a bit—er—?

MRS SOLNESS: I no longer know what to think. The doctor's been telling me so many strange things. And when I think of some of the things I've heard *him* say—

DR HERDAL *looks out through the door.*

HERDAL: Not here yet?

MRS SOLNESS: He'll be back soon. I've sent him a message.

HERDAL (*closer*): You'd better go inside, Mrs Solness.

MRS SOLNESS: No, no. I want to stay out here and wait for Halvard.

HERDAL: Yes, but some ladies have come to see you—

MRS SOLNESS: Oh, my God—no, not now!

HERDAL: They say they simply must watch the ceremony.

MRS SOLNESS: Oh, well, I suppose I'll have to go in to them. It's my duty.

HILDE: Can't you ask them to go away?

MRS SOLNESS: No, no, that's impossible. Since they've come, it's my duty to receive them. You stay out here, though, and talk to him when he gets back.

HERDAL: Yes, talk to him and keep him here as long as possible.

MRS SOLNESS: Yes, do that, please, dear Miss Wangel. Keep him as long as you can.

HILDE: Hadn't you better do it yourself?

MRS SOLNESS: Oh dear, yes—it's *my* duty, really. But one has so many duties—

HERDAL (*looking towards the garden*): Here he is.

MRS SOLNESS: Oh dear, just as I have to go inside!

HERDAL (*to* HILDE): Don't tell him I'm here.

HILDE: Oh, no. I'll find other things to talk about with the master builder.

MRS SOLNESS: And keep him here. I think you can do that better than anyone.

MRS SOLNESS *and* DR HERDAL *go into the house.* HILDE *remains standing on the verandah.* SOLNESS *comes up the steps from the garden.*

SOLNESS: I hear there's someone here who wants to speak to me.

HILDE: Yes, master builder. I want to speak to you.

SOLNESS: Oh, it's you, Hilde. I was afraid it might be Aline and the doctor.

HILDE: You scare very easily, don't you?

SOLNESS: You think so, do you?

HILDE: Yes. People say you're scared of clambering round on the scaffolding.

SOLNESS: That's different.

HILDE: Then you are afraid of it?

SOLNESS: Yes, I am.

HILDE: Afraid you might fall down and kill yourself?

SOLNESS: No, not that.

HILDE: What then?

SOLNESS: I am afraid of retribution, Hilde.

HILDE: Of retribution? (*Shakes her head*) I don't understand.

SOLNESS: Sit down, and I'll tell you something.

HILDE: Yes, tell me. Out with it! (*She sits down on a stool by the railing and looks at him expectantly*).

SOLNESS (*throws his hat on the table*): As you know, I began by building churches.

HILDE (*nods*): Yes, I know that.

SOLNESS: When I was a boy, you see, my parents were pious, country people. So I thought building churches was the finest work that a man could choose to do.

HILDE: Yes, yes.

SOLNESS: And I think I may say that I built these humble little churches with such honesty and tenderness and devotion that—that—

HILDE: That—? Well?

SOLNESS: Yes—that I think He ought to have been pleased with me.

HILDE: He? Which He?

SOLNESS: He whom the churches were meant for, of course. Whose honour and glory they were meant to proclaim.

HILDE: I see. But are you so sure that—that He wasn't—well—pleased with you?

SOLNESS (*scornfully*): *He* pleased with me? How can you talk so foolishly, Hilde? He who let the troll in me cut loose? He who bade them wait on me day and night, these—these—

HILDE: Demons?

SOLNESS: Yes. And the others. Oh, no, I was made to realize He wasn't pleased with me. (*Secretively*) That's why He let the old house be burned down, you see.

HILDE: Was that why?

SOLNESS: Yes, don't you understand? He wanted to give me the chance to be a real master in my own field, and build greater churches to His glory. At first I didn't realize what He wanted. But then, suddenly, it all became clear to me.

HILDE: When was that?

SOLNESS: When I built the church tower up at Lysanger.

HILDE: I thought so.

SOLNESS: You see, Hilde, up there, where I was a stranger, I spent so much time by myself, brooding and puzzling. Then I saw so clearly why He had taken my little children from me. It was so that I should have nothing to bind me. No love or happiness or anything, you see. I was to be a master builder—nothing else. And all my life was to be spent building for Him. (*Laughs*) But that wasn't the way it worked out.

HILDE: What did you do?

SOLNESS: First, I examined and tried myself—

HILDE: And then—?

SOLNESS: Then, like Him, I did the impossible.

HILDE: The impossible?

SOLNESS: I could never bear to climb up high before. But that day, I did it.

HILDE (*jumps up*): Yes, yes, you did!

SOLNESS: And as I stood high up there, right at the top, and placed the wreath over the weathercock, I said to Him: "Listen to me, mighty One! Henceforth I, too, want to be a free master builder. Free in my field, as You are in Yours. I never want to build churches for You again. Only homes, for people to live in."

HILDE (*her eyes wide and glittering*): That was the song I heard in the air.

SOLNESS: But He took His revenge later.

HILDE: What do you mean by that?

SOLNESS (*looks at her dejectedly*): Building homes for people isn't worth twopence, Hilde.

HILDE: How can you say that now?

SOLNESS: Because I realize now that people have no use for the homes they live in. They can't be happy in them. And a home wouldn't have been any use to me—even if I'd had one. (*Laughs quietly and savagely*) So when all the accounts are closed, I have built nothing really. And sacrificed nothing. It all adds up to nothing. Nothing. Nothing.

HILDE: And are you never going to build again?

SOLNESS: Yes, now I shall begin!

HILDE: What will you build? What? Tell me! Quickly!

SOLNESS: Now I shall build the only place where I believe that happiness can exist.

HILDE (*looks at him*): Master builder—you mean our castles in the air.

SOLNESS: Yes. Castles in the air.

HILDE: I'm afraid you'll get giddy before we've climbed halfway.

SOLNESS: Not when I can go hand in hand with you, Hilde.

HILDE: Just with me? Won't there be others?

SOLNESS: What others? What do you mean?

HILDE: Oh—that Kaja at the desk. Poor thing, aren't you going to take her along too?

SOLNESS: Oh. So that's what Aline and you were sitting here talking about!

HILDE: Is it true or isn't it?

SOLNESS (*angrily*): I won't answer that. You must believe in me unquestioningly.

HILDE: I have believed in you for ten years. Unquestioningly.

SOLNESS: You must go on believing in me.

HILDE: Then let me see you stand up there, high and free!

SOLNESS (*heavily*): Oh, Hilde. One can't do things like that every day.

HILDE (*passionately*): But I want you to! I want you to! (*Pleadingly*) Just once more, master builder! Do the impossible again!

SOLNESS (*looks deeply into her eyes*): If I try it, Hilde, I shall stand up there and speak to Him the way I spoke to Him before.

HILDE (*with mounting excitement*): What will you tell Him?

SOLNESS: I shall say to Him; "Hear me, mighty Master! Judge me as You will. But from now on I shall build only one thing—the most beautiful thing in the world—"

HILDE: Yes, yes, yes!

SOLNESS: "I shall build it together with a princess, whom I love—"

HILDE: Yes, tell Him that! Tell Him that!

SOLNESS: I will. And then I shall say to Him: "Now I go down, to take her in my arms and kiss her—"

HILDE: Many times! Tell Him that!

SOLNESS: "Many, many times," I shall tell Him.

HILDE: And then—?

SOLNESS: Then I shall wave my hat—and come down to the ground—and do as I told Him.

HILDE (*flings her arms wide*): Now I see you again as you were when I heard that song in the air!

SOLNESS (*looks at her with bowed head*): How have you come to be what you are, Hilde?

HILDE: How did you make me what I am?

SOLNESS (*curtly, decisively*): The princess shall have her castle.

HILDE (*jubilant, claps her hands*): Oh, master builder! My beautiful, beautiful castle! Our castle in the air!

SOLNESS: Built on a true foundation.

In the street, a crowd of people has gathered; they can be indistinctly glimpsed through the trees. A brass band can be distantly heard from behind the new house. MRS SOLNESS, with a fur collar round her neck, DR HERDAL, carrying her white shawl on his arm, and several LADIES come out on to the verandah. At the same moment, RAGNAR BROVIK comes up from the garden.

MRS SOLNESS (*to* RAGNAR): Are we going to have music, too?

RAGNAR: Yes. It's the Builders' Association. (*To* SOLNESS) The foreman asked me to tell you he's ready to go up with the wreath.

SOLNESS (*takes his hat*): Good. I'll go down there myself.

MRS SOLNESS (*anxiously*): What are you going to do down there, Halvard?

SOLNESS (*curtly*): I must be down below with the men.

MRS SOLNESS: Yes—down below, of course. Down below.

SOLNESS: I always do it. It's my everyday custom. (*He goes down the steps and out through the garden*).

MRS SOLNESS (*shouts over the railing after him*): Do tell the man to be careful when he climbs up! Promise me that, Halvard!

HERDAL (*to* MRS SOLNESS): There, you see, I was right. He's put these mad ideas out of his head.

MRS SOLNESS: Oh, what a relief! Two of our men have fallen. And they were both killed instantaneously. (*Turns to* HILDE) Thank you so much for holding on to him, Miss Wangel. I'd never have been able to budge him.

HERDAL: Yes, yes, Miss Wangel, I'm sure you know how to hold on to someone when you really want to.

MRS SOLNESS and DR HERDAL go over to the LADIES, who are standing by the steps looking out across the garden. HILDE remains standing downstage by the railing. RAGNAR goes across to her.

RAGNAR (*quietly, trying not to laugh*): Do you see all those young men down in the street, Miss—er—?

HILDE: Yes.

RAGNAR: They're my fellow apprentices, come to watch the master.

HILDE: What do they want to watch him for?

RAGNAR: They want to see him not dare to climb up his own house.

HILDE: Is that what the little boys want?

RAGNAR: He's kept us down for so long. Now we want to see him keeping himself down, for a change.

HILDE: You won't. Not this time.

RAGNAR (*smiles*): Oh? Where shall we see him, then?

HILDE: High, high up by the weathercock! That's where you'll see him!

RAGNAR (*laughs*): Him? Not likely!

HILDE: He intends to climb to the top. And you'll see him there.

RAGNAR: Oh, he intends to, I'm sure. But he can't, he just can't. He'd get giddy long before he'd climbed halfway. He'd have to crawl down again on his hands and knees.

HERDAL (*pointing*): Look. There's the foreman climbing up.

MRS SOLNESS: He's got the wreath too. Oh, I do hope he takes care.

RAGNAR (*stares incredulously, then shouts*): But that's not—!

HILDE: (*cries ecstatically*): It's the master builder himself!

MRS SOLNESS (*screams in terror*): Yes, it's Halvard! Oh, my God, my God! Halvard! Halvard!

HERDAL: Ssh! Don't shout to him!

MRS SOLNESS (*almost out of her mind*): I must go to him! I must make him come down!

HERDAL (*restraining her*): Stand still, all of you! Don't make a sound!

HILDE (*standing motionless, follows* SOLNESS *with her eyes*): He's climbing and climbing! Higher—higher! Look! Just look!

RAGNAR (*breathlessly*): He must turn back now! He must!

HILDE: He's climbing, climbing! Soon he'll be up!

MRS SOLNESS: Oh, I shall die of fright. I can't bear to look.

HERDAL: Don't look up at him, then.

HILDE: There he is on top of the scaffolding! Right at the top!

HERDAL: Don't move, anyone! Do you hear?

HILDE (*quiet, but jubilant*): At last! At last! Now I see him great and free again!

RAGNAR (*almost speechless*): But this is—

HILDE: That's how I've seen him all these ten years. How squarely he stands! Frightfully exciting, though! Look at him! Now he's hanging the wreath over the spire!

RAGNAR: But—I can't believe it! This is impossible!

HILDE: Yes! That's what he's doing now! The impossible! (*With the enigmatic expression in her eyes*) Can you see anyone else up there with him?

RAGNAR: There's no one else.

HILDE: Oh, yes. There's someone he's arguing with.

RAGNAR: You're mistaken.

HILDE: Perhaps you can't hear a song in the air, either?

RAGNAR: It must be the wind in the treetops.

HILDE: I hear a song. A mighty song! (*Cries in jubilant ecstasy*) Look, look! Now he's waving his hat! He's waving to us down here! Oh, wave back to him! He's done it at last, he's done it! (*She tears the white shawl from the* DOCTOR, *waves it and cries up*) Hurrah for Solness! Hurrah for the master builder!

HERDAL: Stop it! Stop it, for God's sake—!

The LADIES *on the verandah wave their handkerchiefs, and the shouting is taken up in the street. Suddenly there is a silence; then the crowd utters a shriek of terror. A human body and some planks and poles can be indistinctly glimpsed falling through the trees.*

MRS SOLNESS, LADIES (*simultaneously*): He's falling! He's falling!

MRS SOLNESS *staggers and falls back unconscious. The* LADIES *pick her up amid noise and confusion. The people in the street*

break down the fence and storm into the garden. DR HERDAL
hurries down. Short pause.

HILDE (*still staring upwards, as though turned to stone*): My
master builder!

RAGNAR (*supports himself, trembling, against the railing*): He
must have been smashed to pieces. Killed outright.

ONE OF THE LADIES (*while* MRS SOLNESS *is carried into the
house*): Run down to the doctor—

RAGNAR: I can't move a step—

ANOTHER LADY: Call down to someone, then.

RAGNAR (*tries to shout*): How is he? Is he alive?

A VOICE (*from down in the garden*): The master builder is
dead.

OTHER VOICES (*nearer*): His head was crushed. He fell into
the stonepit.

HILDE (*turns to* RAGNAR, *and says quietly*): Now I can't see
him up there any longer.

RAGNAR: This is terrible. He hadn't the strength after all.

HILDE (*in quiet, crazed triumph*): But he climbed right to the
top! And I heard harps in the air! (*Waves her shawl upwards
and cries wildly and ecstatically*) My—my master builder!

Elizabeth Robins, the American actress who did so much during the eighteen-nineties to promote Ibsen's cause in England, has left a vivid account in her book *Theatre and Friendship* (London, 1932) of the circumstances surrounding the first English production of *The Master Builder*:

"Months before *The Master Builder* reached these shores, the excitement that was set up by mere anticipation will never be credited in these times. . . . Impatience for the play to come was exacerbated by the darkness that shrouded it. . . . Neither the man who had committed himself to publishing it [William Heinemann] nor anybody else had even now the faintest idea what the play would be about. People lived on supposition, and were as hot over it as though they knew what it was they were contending for."

Among the enthusiasts who visited Miss Robins "up those seventy-four steps" for news of the play—the list of names reveals the extent to which the literary world of London had rallied to William Archer's call—were Henry James, Sidney Colvin, Sir Frederick Pollock, Mrs Humphrey Ward, Rhoda Broughton, Bernard Shaw, Gertrude Bell, Herbert Beerbohm Tree, Hubert Crackanthorpe, Arthur Symons and Oscar Wilde. Three pulls of the play (as yet unnamed) were sent from Norway as fast as they were printed—one for Miss Robins and one each for Archer and Edmund Gosse, who had agreed to collaborate on the translation, as they had done with *Hedda Gabler*. "These" wrote Miss Robins, "ultimately arrived in small, in very small, violently agitating spurts—or, as one might say, in volts, projected across the North Sea in a series of electric shocks."

As the pattern of the play gradually emerged, even the most ardent Ibsenites began to have qualms. Miss Robins noted that Archer himself "as well as the rest, is a good deal puzzled;

but he says the first act is powerful and fascinating, though he can't 'see' it on the English stage". As the second act came in "W.A. seems less hopeful. . . . He writes: 'The interest certainly hangs fire, etc., etc.' ". And she added sadly: "*I* fear the thing is hopeless!" Henry James also found the first instalments unpromising. "I have been kindly favoured with the communication of most of it," he wrote to Mrs Hugh Bell, "and am utterly bewildered and mystified. . . . It is all most strange, most curious, most vague, most horrid, most 'middle-classy' in the peculiar ugly Ibsen sense—and alas most *un*promising for Miss Elizabeth or for any *woman*. What is already clear is that a *man* is the central figure . . . and the man, alas, an elderly white-haired architect, or Baumeister, is, although a strange and interesting, a fearfully *charmless* creature."

Miss Robins tried reading the play to Beerbohm Tree, at the Haymarket Theatre. Tree, she reported, "was swept away by Solness, wants to play it"; but it transpired that before doing so he demanded "amazing alterations," to which Heinemann and Archer refused to agree. The lessee of the Lyric Theatre, a Pole named Löwenfelt, agreed to allow Miss Robins to present the play, but negotiations broke down and it was finally staged at the Trafalgar Square Theatre[1] on 20 February 1893.

Trafalgar Square Theatre, 20 *February* 1893

SOLNESS	Herbert Waring
RAGNAR BROVIK	Philip Cuningham
DR HERDAL	John Beauchamp
KNUT BROVIK	Athol Forde
KAJA FOSLI	Marie Linden
MRS SOLNESS	Louise Moodie
HILDE WANGEL	Elizabeth Robins

Produced under the direction of Herbert Waring and Elizabeth Robins

Stage managed by George R. Foss

[1] Now the Duke of York's.

The newspapers greeted the play with a chorus of vituperation.

"Dense mist enshrouds characters, words, actions and motives. . . . One may compare it . . . to the sensations of a man who witnesses a play written, rehearsed and acted by lunatics."
Daily Telegraph

"Platitudes and inanities. . . . The play is hopeless and indefensible."
Globe

"A feast of dull dialogue and acute dementia. . . . The most dreary and purposeless drivel we have ever heard in an English theatre. . . . A pointless, incoherent and absolutely silly piece."
Evening News

"Assuredly no one may fathom the mysteries of the play, so far as it can be called a play. . . . It is not for a moment to be understood that we personally recommend anyone to go and see it."
Standard

"Rigmarole of an Oracle Delphic in obscurity and Gamp-like in garrulity. . . . Pulseless and purposeless play, which has idiocy written on every lineament. . . . Three acts of gibberish."
Stage

"Sensuality . . . irreverence . . . unwholesome . . . simply blasphemous."
Morning Post

"Dull, mysterious, unchaste." *Daily Graphic*

On the day after the opening performance, Henry James wrote to Elizabeth Robins:

"I have looked at the papers, and there is little edification in them of course. They are stupid, angry and mean. The weaknesses of the play do indeed come out strongly in representation, but it would have been only honest in them to acknowledge also its *hold*, the odd baffling spell it works and the remarkable spell of the interpretation. . . . I thought Waring *extremely* good—various and interesting, intelligent and coloured: BUT distinctly not loud enough. You were—keep it up, *up*, UP. Miss M. disappointing—entirely too monotonously and conventionally tragic—making poor Mrs S. a stale theatrical *category*, instead of a special person. The *doll* scene with you, in Act III, is rendered very dangerous by her slow intensity of solemnity. But there is no doubt the play does what one expected it would do—of course it doesn't do what one didn't. It lives and makes its life felt on the consenting. The others were out of account from the 1st. I see the *Telegraph* and the *Chronicle* have some liberality. But it is in 'theatrical circles'—or with the independent spectator that your own achievement will tell."

However, when James revisited the theatre for a subsequent performance he noted to his delight and surprise that "the house was *full*." George Moore wrote to Elizabeth Robins: "I thank God I came a second time. It has grown upon me. I understand." Indeed, he came a third time. Oscar Wilde attended the final performance and was greatly impressed. On 6 March the play was transferred to the evening bill at the Vaudeville.

Charles Archer, in his biography of his brother, William Archer, commented: "The piece had indeed a somewhat mixed reception. It cut across the Ibsenite and anti-Ibsenite ranks, disconcerting some adherents (Walkley among others), while it made a number of influential converts. But, being admirably acted by Miss Robins as Hilde and Mr Waring as Solness, it had a real success, as success went in such special productions, and the interest aroused by it led to a series of subscription performances in June—the plays given being *Hedda Gabler*, *Rosmersholm*, *The Master Builder* and the 4th Act of *Brand*."

Opera Comique, 2 *June* 1893

SOLNESS	Lewis Waller
RAGNAR BROVIK	Scott Buist

Dr Herdal	Charles Sugden
Knut Brovik	Leonard Outram
Kaja Fosli	Marie Linden
Mrs Solness	Frances Ivor
Hilde Wangel	Elizabeth Robins

Stage managed by George R. Foss

"Mr Lewis Waller . . . has every qualification for an admirable Solness, if he will only throw himself into the part with confidence and energy. He played it on Friday last under grave disadvantages, having had very scant time for preparation."

William Archer in the *World*

The programme, in giving credit to the joint translators, misprinted Edmund Gosse as Yosse.

Gentlemen's Concert Hall, Manchester, 30 November 1894

The Manchester Independent Theatre Committee invited Elizabeth Robins to present *The Master Builder* in their city. I have not succeeded in tracing a programme of this production, or in discovering who played the two Broviks; Solness was taken by Acton Bond, Dr Herdal by Charles Sugden, Mrs Solness by Alexes Leighton and Kaja Fosli by Florence Farr.

"Mr Acton Bond, as Solness, grasped the necessity to represent distraction, but missed the subtleties . . . Miss Elizabeth Robins has now wrought herself firmly, and we may say absolutely, into the part of Hilda Wangel, as she chooses to conceive it, and as, perhaps, it is alone possible to play it credibly. So far we can speak without stint, but we differ from the common opinion that Miss Robins duly fills the character which the *reader* is compelled to imagine. She has voice, grace of movement, wit, and a charm that is shrewish when that is necessary; she can fully express an irresponsible desire for the 'joy of life.' This was enough for the audience; it carried them away; it was all they tried to understand; but it is only half the character. Ibsen really presents that character as full of discords; it has not only the qualities shown by Miss Robins, but a strain of human sympathy and of distaste for ugly actions, and, in short, of spiritual fineness . . .

"In our belief, the arrival here of Miss Robins and her company is rather an important theatrical event, and their acting has a claim to more respect and study than it has in all quarters received. It is possible to dislike Ibsen, but people ought to go and see his dramas, if only because Ibsen has the power of creating actors; and the more intelligent actors we can get here the better."

Oliver Elton in the Manchester Guardian

Opera Comique, 27 *March* 1895

(Guest performance by the Théâtre de L'Oeuvre de Paris, at the invitation of the Independent Theatre).

SOLNESS	M. Lugné-Poe
RAGNAR BROVIK	M. Nargeot
DR HERDAL	M. Ripert
KNUT BROVIK	(not named in programme)
KAJA FOSLI	Mdlle Marthe Mellot
MRS SOLNESS	Mme Suzanne Gay
HILDE WANGEL	Mdlle Suzanne Despres

Produced by M. Lugné-Poe

"Comparing the performance with that which we have achieved in England, it must be admitted that neither Mr Waring nor Mr Waller were in a position to play Solness as M. Lugné-Poe played him. They would never have got another engagement in genteel comedy if they had worn those vulgar trousers, painted that red eruption on their faces, and given life to that portrait which, in every stroke, from its domineering energy, talent and covetousness, to its half-witted egoism and crazy philandering sentiment, is so amazingly true to life. Mr Waring and Mr Waller failed because they were under the spell of Ibsen's fame as a dramatic magician, and grasped at his poetic treatment of the man instead of at the man himself. M. Lugné-Poe succeeded because he recognized Solness as a person he had met a dozen times in ordinary life, and just reddened his nose and played him without preoccupation.

"With Hilde it was a different matter. Except for the first five minutes, in which she was so bright and girlish, Mdlle. Despres could not touch Miss Robins as Hilde Wangel. . . . It is an essential part of Hilde that she does not realize her own humanity, much less that of the poor wretch whom she destroys, or the woman whom she widows both before and after his actual bodily death. This merciless insensibility, which gives such appalling force to youth, and which, when combined with vivid imagination, high brain power, and personal fascination, makes the young person in search of the 'frightfully thrilling' more dangerous than a lion in the path, was presented by Miss Robins with such reality that she made *The Master Builder* seem almost a one-part play. . . . A Hilde who can even approach Miss Robins has not yet been seen in London."

Bernard Shaw in the *Saturday Review*

The previous autumn (1894), Lugné-Poe had ventured to take this production to Norway and play Solness in the presence of Ibsen himself (with Mme Berthe Bady as Hilde). Halvdan Koht has recorded the scene. "Through the first act Ibsen sat still and immovable; but in the second act, as the action between Hilde and Solness mounted higher and higher with an impulse of love that swept like a storm over their souls, Ibsen rose involuntarily and his eyes riveted themselves on the actors, so that they felt the fire of his look and caught from it even more fervour than before. In the third act he sat leaning far out over the edge of the box. It was the triumph of *The Master Builder*. 'This,' said Ibsen, 'was the resurrection of my play.'"

Bijou Theatre, 17 *September* 1907

SOLNESS	Leigh Lovel
RAGNAR BROVIK	A. Hylton Allen

DR HERDAL	Julian Cross
KNUT BROVIK	Arthur Chesney
KAJA FOSLI	Dora Levis
MRS SOLNESS	Ethel Caryllon
HILDE WANGEL	Octavia Kenmore

Produced by Leigh Lovel

Leigh Lovel and his wife, Octavia Kenmore, were great Ibsen enthusiasts and gave many provincial audiences their first taste of his work.

Court Theatre, 16 *March* 1909 (single performance)

SOLNESS	Rathmell Wilson
RAGNAR BROVIK	A. E. Filmer
DR HERDAL	Ross Shore
KNUT BROVIK	Campbell Cargill
KAJA FOSLI	Beatrice Filmer
MRS SOLNESS	Winefride Borrow
HILDE WANGEL	Jessica Salomon

Produced by Charles Charrington

Little Theatre, 28 *March* 1911

SOLNESS	Norman McKinnel
RAGNAR BROVIK	Harcourt Williams
DR HERDAL	Claude King
KNUT BROVIK	Leon M. Lion
KAJA FOSLI	Christine Silver
MRS SOLNESS	Katherine Pole
HILDE WANGEL	Lillah McCarthy

Produced by Granville Barker

"The play, after all these years, gave us great pleasure; in fact, more so than ever before, for our actors have learned much. Formerly, when the Ibsen method was unknown to the players and a half-sealed book to the producers, the performance displayed respectful declamation. The idea was

116

there, but not its vitalization. Hence, perhaps, the melancholy fact that it has taken England as many decades to appreciate Ibsen as the Continent took years. . . . The performance at the Little Theatre was fine as a whole, if not faultless in some respects. But the stage management reflects infinite credit on Mr Granville Barker. The smaller parts were all excellently rendered. . . . Of the English Hilde Wangels, Miss Lillah McCarthy's is the most remarkable. I could imagine another personality. I could not imagine a performance more profoundly studied, variegated, intense, bubbling over with the joy of life and causing us to feel the magnetic coil of ambition at work in the soul of budding womanhood. . . . Mr Norman McKinnel's Solness . . . contained consistent, solid, sometimes powerful good work, but it lacked the great spark which marks the rise and fall of Solness and made him, for a time, a leader of men. . . ."

J. T. Grein in the *Sunday Times*

Court Theatre, 13 *May* 1918

SOLNESS	Leigh Lovel
RAGNAR BROVIK	Laurence Andrews
DR HERDAL	Sydney Paxton
KNUT BROVIK	Orlando Barnett
KAJA FOSLI	Ray Litvin
MRS SOLNESS	Ida Phillips
HILDE WANGEL	Octavia Kenmore

Produced by Leigh Lovel

Playhouse Theatre, Oxford, 19 *November* 1923

SOLNESS	Earle Grey
RAGNAR BROVIK	Peter Cresswell
DR HERDAL	Reginald Denham
KNUT BROVIK	Richard Goolden
KAJA FOSLI	Flora Robson

Mrs Solness	Florence Buckton
Hilde Wangel	Jane Ellis

Produced by Reginald Denham

"Mr Earle Grey . . . acted in an inspired way. Miss Florence Buckton was equally remarkable as Mrs. Solness. Her very footsteps were charged with Ibsen's gloom and her voice had a fine shivery quality which echoed deep down in the heart. Praise is also due to Miss Jane Ellis, Miss Flora Robson and Mr Richard Goolden."

Cherwell

Repertory Theatre, Birmingham, 11 *October* 1924

Solness	Edgar Norfolk
Ragnar Brovik	Paget Hunter
Dr Herdal	Frank Moore
Knut Brovik	Stringer Davis
Kaja Fosli	Cecile Dixon
Mrs Solness	Marjorie Gabain
Hilde Wangel	Gwen Ffrangcon-Davies

Produced by H. K. Ayliff

"A strong and interesting performance. Mr Edgar Norfolk, with a most flexible and persuasive voice, was finely human as the Master Builder. Miss Gwen Ffrangcon-Davies . . . endowed Hilde with an uncanny selfishness which, although debatable, kept the action on the spiritual plane instead of the physical."

Birmingham Post

Q Theatre, 11 *June* 1928

Solness	Victor Lewisohn
Ragnar Brovik	Walter Schofield
Dr Herdal	Arthur Ewart
Knut Brovik	Cyril Hardingham
Kaja Fosli	Primrose Morgan
Mrs Solness	Nora Nicholson
Hilde Wangel	Delia Delvina

Produced by Mrs J. T. Grein

Everyman Theatre, 4 October 1928

SOLNESS	Charles Carson
RAGNAR BROVIK	Perceval Clark
DR HERDAL	Frank Moore
KNUT BROVIK	Hugh E. Wright
KAJA FOSLI	Phyllis Pearson
MRS SOLNESS	Maud Jolliffe
HILDE WANDEL	Florence McHugh

Produced by Malcolm Morley

"It is the peculiar excellence of Mr Malcolm Morley's production that these surging significances break through, ever and anon making us aware of Ibsen's spiritual theme, yet never arresting the interest in the human character. The Master Builder of Mr Charles Carson is a brilliantly conceived study, freshly revealing the human frailties in the light of gentle humour and the sharper flame of acid observation."

J. T. Grein in the *Sketch*

Duchess Theatre, 19 *November* 1931 (People's National Theatre)

SOLNESS	Victor Lewisohn
RAGNAR BROVIK	Eric Portman
DR HERDAL	Walter Piers
KNUT BROVIK	H. O. Nicholson
KAJA FOSLI	Jean Atholl
MRS SOLNESS	Mary Merrall
HILDE WANGEL	Agatha Kentish

Produced by Malcolm Morley

"Miss Nancy Price is a brave lady who keeps the word which she has pledged. Having pledged her word to produce *The Master Builder* on Thursday last, she produced it, despite the regrettable and unavoidable inability to appear of Mr Franklin Dyall who was to have played Solness, and Miss Lydia Sherwood who was billed for Hilde Wangel. 'Safety Last' is a gallant motto, but even this would not have availed

Miss Price if it had not been for the astonishing intrepidity and devotion of Mr. Victor Lewisohn, who in something under eight hours mugged up the part of Solness, while Miss Agatha Kentish did the ladylike equivalent for Hilde. . . . Mr Lewisohn succeeded brilliantly, because he is an Ibsen actor, which means an actor capable of suggesting immensities of mind at work. . . . Miss Kentish did very well too, and there was a faultless performance of Mrs Solness by Miss Mary Merrall."

James Agate in the Sunday Times

Duchess Theatre, 25 *November* 1931

Cast as on 19 November 1931, except that Solness was played by Franklin Dyall, Hilde Wangel by Beatrix Thomson, and Kaja Fosli by Agatha Kentish.

"Mr Dyall can look more hag-ridden than any other actor on the stage, and in this respect it would be difficult to find a better Solness. Where he fell short was perhaps in persuading us of the Master Builder's charm. . . . Was Miss Beatrix Thomson at times too much the bird of prey, too little the wild birds of the woods? The question remains, but there was no doubt of the ability with which she and Mr Dyall carried through their long duet."

Observer (unsigned review)

Westminster Theatre, 15 *April* 1934

(Single performance by The Scandinavian Theatre)

SOLNESS	Donald Wolfit
RAGNAR BROVIK	John Clements
DR HERDAL	Frank Darch
KNUT BROVIK	Alfred Sangster
KAJA FOSLI	Elspeth March
MRS SOLNESS	Margaret Rutherford
HILDE WANGEL	Margaret Webster

Produced by Donald Wolfit

"Mr Wolfit . . . threw himself about a little too much physically and not quite enough emotionally, but his sincerity and his grasp of the part were unimpeachable. Miss Webster was still better. Her Hilde Wangel was admirable in every way—except for the unfortunate fact that she could not look the part. Margaret Rutherford, who was Mrs Solness . . . played the part as if she were Mrs Gummidge doing Ophelia's mad scene—and heightened the impression by clinging firmly to a bunch of withered flowers."

W. A. Darlington in the *Daily Telegraph*

Embassy Theatre, 30 April 1934

Cast as at Westminster Theatre on 15 April 1934, except that Beatrix Lehmann played Hilde, and Donald Wolfit produced in co-operation with Esmé Church.

"I was especially struck by Miss Margaret Rutherford's livid portrait of Mrs Solness, warped slave of duty, dreamer whose dreams are dead. Mr Donald Wolfit's Solness is excellent because it so vividly reveals the flimsiness of the man's strength; it has the right crazy fire which gives flashlight without substantial heat. Miss Beatrix Lehmann is perfectly cast as Hilde Wangel, for, with her sharp, expressive profile and her eyes all eloquence, she can be at once the ecstatic worshipper and remorseless bird of prey. Many Hildes have been industriously 'fey'; none, in my experience, so essentially the falcon, a thing of air as well as of fire, demonic, taloned, soaring."

Ivor Brown in the *Observer*

Criterion Theatre, 12 March 1936

SOLNESS	D. A. Clarke-Smith
RAGNAR BROVIK	Geoffrey Edwards
DR HERDAL	Wilfred Grantham
KNUT BROVIK	John Rae
KAJA FOSLI	Pauline Vilda
MRS SOLNESS	Marjorie Gabain
HILDE WANGEL	Lydia Lopokova

Produced by Irene Hentschel

"Mme Lydia Lopokova and Mr D. Clarke-Smith . . . give performances of remarkable freshness and vigour. Mr Clarke-Smith rightly will not allow that Solness is a 'stodgy' character. He gives him a hard, ruthless intelligence and a genuine imaginative fire that flashes out among his self-deceptions and his conscious vanities, and he also discovers in the man what surely has always been there, an under-current of dry comedy. Mme Lopokova, for her part, refuses to play Hilde on the single note of impishness and irre-sponsible desire for the 'joy of life'. The needed touch of charm is there, and we get more than a hint of spiritual fineness struggling in a discordant nature."

The Times

Westminster Theatre, 29 *June* 1943

SOLNESS	Donald Wolfit
RAGNAR BROVIK	Richard Lyndhurst
DR HERDAL	Eric Adeney
KNUT BROVIK	Henry Fielding
KAJA FOSLI	Adza Vincent
MRS SOLNESS	Christine Silver
HILDE WANDEL	Rosalind Iden

Produced by Donald Wolfit

"War-time audiences have already reason to be grateful to Mr Donald Wolfit, and it is only in the spirit of his record that he should now bring back to the stage the greatest tragedy of our time. . . . Mr Wolfit and Miss Rosalind Iden work well together, and her occasional falter does not disturb his balance. When, with a spirit of devil-may-care as his own once was, she flings him the challenge which he must take up or confess to life's failure, the audience is left in no doubt as to the tragedy's application to the life of sinful man. So clear and exciting an interpretation calls for big audiences, in a day of big audiences."

The Times

SOLNESS	Frederick Valk
RAGNAR BROVIK	Donald Houston
DR HERDAL	Oliver Burt
KNUT BROVIK	Noel Howlett
KAJA FOSLI	Yvonne Mitchell
MRS SOLNESS	Jane Henderson
HILDE WANGEL	Valerie White

Produced by Peter Ashmore

"Mr Frederick Valk's superbly flamboyant playing of Halvard Solness reminds us that the necessary basis of the Master Builder's destructive genius is a superabundant vitality. As much by this uncomfortable power as by untoward circumstance has he destroyed himself and others for his art, and it is the same power which has led him to misuse that art itself.

"It is upon the drab side of the character that most English actors concentrate. So concerned are they to reproduce the fear and remorse that are overtaking the sick and ageing artist that they are always in danger of belittling the spirit struggling to the last against retribution. And a moribund man makes a poor stage figure. Mr. Valk brings Solness completely to life. His own vitality is such that a vehement outburst or a pounce of irascibility sometimes seems to shake the theatre, as though it were an outhouse with a power-engine inside; but the performance never at any moment falls into the sound and fury that signify nothing. His Solness is a man in whose genius and reckless charm we can believe; the remnants of those qualities are there along with the remorse bred of age and introspection and the fantastic fear of youth, and the still more fantastic craving for it. . . .

"Miss Valerie White's Hilde Wangel is not easily to be bettered. . . . She is in love, not with the man, but with greatness, as he is in love with youth. And so the great middle act goes without a flaw—and with the superb momentum and flamboyance that it gains from Mr Valk's masterfully complete grasp of his part."

The Times

Westminster Theatre, 14 May 1948

SOLNESS	Donald Wolfit
RAGNAR BROVIK	David Dodimead
DR HERDAL	Robert Algar
KNUT BROVIK	Frederick Horrey
KAJA FOSLI	Josephine Fraser
MRS SOLNESS	Josephine Wilson
HILDE WANGEL	Rosalind Iden

Produced by Peter Cotes

"Mr Donald Wolfit's travels bring him ashore in Ibsen's Norway, but without a company of equals he must not expect to reach its heights. It is one part, not the play, that he revives. An able intelligence inspires his Solness. Passage after passage shows the mettlesome and tormented creature alive, pacing its cage, hammering at the bars, and then suddenly relaxing in the calm that comes if one will only look failure in the face. In the last act there are moments when this Solness is very good indeed. But Mr Wolfit . . . is always taking leave of his Solness and going off into fits of stage excitement in which he huffs and he puffs until he blows the illusion away. What is remarkable is the power of the performance somehow to survive these lapses."

The Times

B.B.C. Television, 2 May 1950

SOLNESS	Roger Livesey
RAGNAR BROVIK	Geoffrey Keen
DR HERDAL	Charles Maunsell
KNUT BROVIK	Harcourt Williams
KAJA FOSLI	Jill Balcon

MRS SOLNESS Catherine Lacey
HILDE WANGEL Adila Mandlova
Produced by Royston Morley

A.B.C. Television, 19 *January* 1958

SOLNESS André Morell
RAGNAR BROVIK Patrick Troughton
DR HERDAL Oliver Burt
KNUT BROVIK Keith Pyott
KAJA FOSLI Christine Finn
MRS SOLNESS Marie Ney
HILDE WANGEL Mary Peach

Produced by Dennis Vance

B.B.C. Television, 23 *February* 1958

SOLNESS Donald Wolfit
RAGNAR BROVIK David Markham
DR HERDAL Clive Morton
KNUT BROVIK Harold Scott
KAJA FOSLI Elaine Usher
MRS SOLNESS Catherine Lacey
HILDE WANGEL Mai Zetterling

Produced by Stephen Harrison

NOTE ON THE TRANSLATION

In the volumes published previously in this series (*Brand,
The Lady from the Sea, John Gabriel Borkman* and *When We
Dead Awaken*) I have apologized for allowing myself a certain
amount of liberty as regards cutting, necessitated by Ibsen's
tendency to underline and repeat his points to a degree which
today would sound tiresomely repetitive. *The Master Builder*,
however, is, with the possible exception of *Hedda Gabler*, the
most tautly written of all Ibsen's plays, and apart from the
excision of occasional tautologies the main problem presented
to a translator is that of conveying Solness's style of speech.
He is a self-man man of humble country upbringing who
normally speaks with a gruff abruptness; but in the long dia-
logues with Hilde he finds himself groping in unfamiliar
territory and achieving a rough and slightly awkward eloquence. Although, generally speaking, English dialects should
be avoided in the translation and presentation of foreign
plays, I think a case could be made out for playing Solness
with a north country or Scottish accent. Hilde speaks in the
unfamiliar idiom of the new generation; and I would ask
anyone who suspects that I have allowed her too many
modernisms to remember that *The Master Builder* was written
in the same year as *Charley's Aunt*.

A word about trolls. Solness's repeated references to them
are meaningless unless one has a clear understanding of what
the word means. Professor Francis Bull, the greatest of Ibsen
scholars, defined them admirably in a lecture delivered at
Oxford in 1954:

"Trolls—what are they? The word cannot be translated at
all! The trolls are supernatural beings, akin to the enemies of
the gods in the heathen world, and very well known in Norwegian fairy-tales and folk-lore. They are supposed to live

in the woods and mountains, and you must not imagine them in the shape of little goblins; they look more like Polyphemus and Cyclops in the *Odyssey*—huge, clumsy and ugly. . . . [They] may be said to represent the evil forces in Nature, at first only as incarnations of frightening sounds and visions from without, but in more recent literature gradually taken in a wider sense, embodying or symbolizing those powers of evil, hidden in the soul of man, which may at times suddenly suppress his conscious will and dominate his actions. A great Norwegian novelist and friend of Ibsen has written two volumes of short stories and fairy tales, simply called *Trolls*, starting with this declaration: 'That there are trolls in Man, everybody knows who has any insight into such things'. . . . In . . . *The Master Builder*, which is very much the author's personal confession, Solness, half in joke and half in earnest and remorse, tells about his devils or trolls; in a way they serve him, but by ever pandering to his evil instincts and desires they have come to be really his rulers—mysterious powers that make him afraid of himself."

I again gladly acknowledge my thanks to Mr Casper Wrede for much invaluable criticism and more shrewd suggestions than I can enumerate.

M.M.